SCIENCE, TECHNOLOGY AND
THE CHRISTIAN

SCIENCE, TECHNOLOGY AND
THE CHRISTIAN

by

C. A. COULSON, F.R.S.

ABINGDON PRESS
NEW YORK . NASHVILLE

SET IN MONOTYPE SCOTCH ROMAN AND PRINTED IN
GREAT BRITAIN BY THE CAMELOT PRESS LTD
LONDON AND SOUTHAMPTON

CONTENTS

Prologue

A WORD OF explanation is needed for this little book. Science and Technology are both vast subjects, whose complete description would require a much larger account than I can give. I cannot help remembering that the immense Oxford *History of Technology* alone ran to five volumes of about 1000 pages each. The relation of all this to the Christian faith that I hold is a complex one that touches nearly all of the ordinary activities of my life, and in addition I can lay no claim to being a social scientist. The excuse for writing this book is that I believe it to be exceedingly important in any democracy that ordinary people should know enough about the factors which affect and influence their lives as will enable them to recognize the problems which have to be solved. It is no good recognizing these problems too late to be able to deal with them properly.

Yet this is precisely what happened in the first industrial revolution. There would not otherwise have been such appalling standards of home building nor such unsatisfactory working conditions for a large part of our population. We suffer the reward for our former lack of imagination in the existence of ugly, characterless, unhealthy manufacturing towns; and in a serious debasement of the value which we attach to ordinary honest work. It would indeed be tragic if the moral of those earlier failures were not heeded now, as we move into a new industrial revolution. Someone must speak, in words which can be easily understood. Someone must show that the problems are different now from what they were then, but they require for their solution more imagination rather than less. Someone must claim that the Christian, just because he believes that this is God's world, must state his case, and show how the interpretation of some of the great Christian principles of conduct bears on such matters as the control of nuclear power, the implications of automation or the feeding of a huge and hungry world. If it be asserted that the Christian, as such, has no special knowledge of science, or technology, or of the politics which will be necessary in order to translate them into action, I shall reply that the politician can do nothing until he is supported—and often gingered—by a lively and informed public opinion. Every Christian should have his part to play in forming this opinion. Do we not claim that God's revelation in Jesus Christ gives us the clue whereby we understand God's will for our world? How then do we dare to keep silence when the scientists and technologists are fashioning the tools for a new earth? The tremendous involvement of science and technology in the pattern of our lives is sufficient justification for a Beckly lecturer to try to relate them to our more fundamental Christian beliefs. Others, with more expert knowledge of particular items, must etch in the details of the picture: my concern is to show that there is an outline of this picture which can be drawn in simple terms. If I am right in the claims that I am making, it follows that Christians have a peculiarly significant role to play. For without the insights which they possess wrong decisions are certain to be made. But now, just because our civilization is so much more complex, the penalty for wrong-doing in this way is more severe than it was. It is important, therefore, that we have available for our use such facts as will help us to decide, and decide rightly. The object of this book is to provide some of these basic facts, to show the nature of the issues that are involved, and the manner in which Christians contribute to the solution of the problems associated with them. But of course no one 'knows all the answers'. I suspect that there will be errors, of fact or of judgement, in what I have written. I hope to be informed of these, so that I may correct my faulty thinking. But I hope also that my fellow-Christians will be stimulated to see that in this moment of quite exceptional significance for the future, they have a real and significant contribution to make. There are many ways in which we have to serve our generation: thinking sensibly and creatively about the future is not the least among them.

CHAPTER ONE

Technology in the first and second Industrial Revolutions[1]

THE TWENTIETH century is a quite unique event. For it shows us to be at the beginning of a change in the pattern of our living which will grow until it becomes greater than any previous change has ever been. It would be no exaggeration to call it the Second Industrial Revolution. If we are to see these changes in their true perspective we shall have to compare this second industrial revolution with the more familiar first one. Such a comparison is necessary if we are to recognize the factors which operate in shaping the future. These factors are almost totally different in our second industrial revolution from what they were in the first.

The first industrial revolution is usually dated between 1750 and 1900. But of course any such precise dating is really impossible, since the development of industry was a slow process. Before 1750, however, the industrial state did not exist. Britain was still largely agricultural, and Napoleon could refer to us as 'a nation of shopkeepers'. But by 1815, thanks to her inventive genius and her control of the seas, she had won the title of 'workshop of the world'. In 1851 the Great Exhibition in Hyde Park was a demonstration to all the world that

[1] A large part of the material of this chapter is reproduced from a lecture to science teachers which I gave in Oxford for the Institute of Education in July 1959, and which is to be printed in *Science as a General Study in the Sixth Form*. I am grateful for permission to include it here.

in machinery and technical innovation she was un-disputed leader. By 1900, however, the fruits of this revolution were much more uniformly shared among the nations of the West, and pure science was beginning to intrude. At that time no one could see how meteoric this rise of science would be, nor the profound influence it would subsequently have on technology. That is why the discovery of the electron in 1897 and of X-rays a year earlier are best thought of as heralding the birth-day of the second revolution in which we are now living.

It is worth while to spend a little time reminding ourselves of the changes that the first industrial revolu-tion brought. This can be done very easily by turning to the pages of a magazine such as the *Scientific American*. Thus, in April of 1849 we read that 'the ship *Sea Witch* has just completed a voyage round the world in 194 days of sailing'. That time was still about twenty-five years before Jules Verne had written his *Round the World in Eighty Days*. But, slow as it was, it was vastly quicker than a hundred years earlier. For in 1750 the coaching time from Birmingham to London was three days, and from London to Edinburgh nearly a week.

Compare this situation with what can happen now. During the last year I have twice had occasion to visit America. On one of the new jet aeroplanes we left London Airport at 11 a.m. and had touched down at Idlewild International Airport, New York by 2 p.m. Even allowing for the change of five hours in local time between London and New York, this is a pretty remark-able achievement. But if I travel, as I hope to do, over the same journey in another ten years, I shall probably arrive before I have started—by local time!—for plans

are relatively far advanced to make commercial air
transport that will fly at about 2000 m.p.h., and reduce
to about one and a half hours the time for the Atlantic
crossing.

In the same issue of *Scientific American*, 1849, there is
an account of the first typewriter.

We have recently had the pleasure of examining a small,
but very ingenious machine, recently invented by Mr Oliver
T. Eddy, which promises, when perfected, to be of very great
utility. It is an instrument which will print, with almost the
perfection of an ordinary printing press, a single copy of any
document, and with about the same rapidity as the document
can be transcribed by a good penman. They are played on,
as it were, striking keys answering to the letters of the
alphabet, and the response is the instantaneous impression
on the sheet.

There could have been little effective industry without the typewriter, and its most important adjunct,
carbon paper. For this systematized the keeping of
correspondence and records. But, important as it is, it
pales before the present situation. I am told that it
takes a bare two minutes to go through the whole process
involved in printing one Penguin book. And as for the
business of typing, modern computing equipment is such
that up to twenty pages of writing may be typed by a
high-speed machine within about one minute. In a few
years' time all the book-keeping and all the accounts of
the larger banks will be performed by one electronic
computer, far more rapidly and accurately than at
present, and connected by telephone wires to each
separate branch.

Let us turn from 1850 to the beginning of the present
century, and compare the situation then, as our second

industrial revolution was just beginning, with the situation as we know it now, sixty years later. In the same journal as before we now read that 'neon, krypton and argon have been isolated from liquid air'. In other words we were just beginning to understand the fundamental nature of the environment in which we lived. For thousands of years, without a moment's thought, man had breathed; but now he was coming to grips with the ultimate secret of the air, for so long hidden from him, and it would not be long before he splashed the knowledge of his success in blood-red neon signs around Piccadilly Circus.

Or again, in the same issue of this journal:

Marconi has just telegraphed without wires across the English Channel. . . . In view of the visionary speculation that has been indulged in by some of the investigators of wireless telegraphy, there is something decidedly refreshing in the businesslike methods and practical results which have characterized the work of this brilliant young Italian.

What a change in the fifty years since then! Now anything that any statesman or politician says anywhere in the world belongs to the whole world in less than a second. If he speaks in a large hall, his words may actually be heard by wireless in the Antipodes before they reach his audience in the back row. Our world has become one back-yard. It is part of our new age that we must learn to think in terms of this unaccustomed intimacy. It would indeed be odd if we were not puzzled by our new responsibility.

I cannot forbear to quote once more from the *Scientific American*, this time of 1904.

Uranium is one of the rare metals for which there is a limited demand. The present world consumption amounts annually to about 300 tons of ore, yielding 10-40 tons of the metal. For several years Colorado has supplied the U.S. output, nearly all of which goes to Europe. France, England, and Germany are the principal markets.

Again what a change! For here is the very beginning of our knowledge of the heavy atoms, out of whose fission we are now winning undreamt supplies of nuclear power. But notice how significant this scientific knowledge was to be in influencing the shape of our community, as soon as it could become technological. For the first industrial revolution was built very largely upon the use of coal and, later, of oil. Now these are not particularly convenient fuels. Especially in the case of coal, their transport is a nuisance, so that almost inevitably we built our towns and our industrial areas near to where the coal could be mined. This cannot be extended to all the other countries of the world in the same way that it grew up in Britain. For example, almost all the 'natural' fuels in the earth's crust are to be found north of the Equator. If the population which lives south of this line and in India is to enjoy the same access to coal and oil as we in the northern zones enjoy, it will be necessary each year to transport millions of tons of coal. In precise terms, if India alone used as much coal per head as we do, we should need to carry one thousand million tons every year. Such a prospect is quite impracticable, even supposing that so much coal could be brought to the pithead surface. We can therefore see that nothing less than almost complete nuclear power supply will be inevitable for a large part of the world. Without it, not only would our own civilization slowly grind to a halt, but there would be no foreseeable development in the under-developed countries of the world. Yet the fact that the fuel for an atomic reactor weighs only a relatively small number of tons per year (there is fuel-equivalent to 1,300 tons of coal in one pound of uranium!) implies that we are no longer so restricted in the location of our power stations. Already we see a liberating influence released by the new knowledge on which our present revolution is based. And at the same time we begin to recognize that, even if they themselves do not always notice the fact, the scientists and technologists are the inescapable agents of many of the changes in our pattern of life. In the words of Professor D. G. Christopherson,

A case can be made for the view that, when universal history is written in a thousand years' time, the most influential Englishmen will be seen to be not Cromwell and Pitt, not even Shakespeare and Milton, but Newton and Watt and Faraday.

I do not believe that I could go quite so far as this myself, for it is still true that man does not live by bread alone. But I have no hesitations about the rest of the same paragraph:

If, by that time, men can be sure that the industrial revolution represented, for all its excesses, a necessary step in evolution towards a better age, it will be the British people, to a greater extent than any other group of similar size, who will deserve the credit for having initiated that step, and if the developments of the last two hundred years turn out to have been a terrible error and deviation in human history, it is we who will bear a large part of the responsibility.

I have been describing some of the technical differences between the two industrial revolutions. It is now necessary to comment on some of the influences which these revolutions have exerted both on our national life and on ordinary people.

My first comment concerns the relation between science and technology. By science I mean the fundamental knowledge of our world and its environment, the controlled and steady search for knowledge, without any necessary desire to use it for public ends: I am thinking of the sort of enquiry that we associate with a university, though the spirit behind it may also be traced in certain Government research laboratories, and in many of the central research organizations set up by individual industries. And by technology I mean the concentrated, relentless study of the ways in which things may be made, or changed: or the new knowledge of science may be pressed into human service. It is science when measurements are made of the number of neutrons emitted in the break-up of a nucleus of the uranium atom, but it is technology when this knowledge is used to design the moderators in an atomic pile from which, as in Calder Hall, we expect to feed energy into the national electricity grid. Similarly, it is science when a group of X-ray workers are able to determine the atomic arrangement in the molecule of penicillin—as we might say, its molecular architecture—but it is technology when we seek the most efficient way of growing the mould in which this substance may be found, so that factories may be built, and large amounts of the antibiotic made available to cure disease.

I want to suggest that the relation between science and technology in our second revolution is quite different from what it was in our first. This will show the much profounder influence which we must anticipate for the present and future as compared with that which we have already experienced in the past. It will also suggest, for our later consideration, that any control over modern technology will require a totally different outlook and technique from that appropriate (though not always adopted) in earlier periods.

In the 'old' days—which is a pleasant pseudonym for 'pre-1900'—technology depended very little upon science. The Iron Age and the Bronze Age date from the pre-Christian era, centuries before the scientist had any inkling of what a metal was 'really' like. Instead of science there was the art of the craftsman. Anyone who had contacts with the heavy industry of this country will know how much hit-and-miss there was in industrial technique. When I was a boy, I lived in the Black Country, the large industrial belt just north of Birmingham. One of my father's most respected friends was consultant for several iron and steel firms. Yet this gentleman had not the least grain of fundamental scientific knowledge: he had never contributed a single paper to any of the scientific journals of this country. He had lived, and grown up, surrounded by people who were similarly ignorant of the fundamentals: but who, like him, possessed an uncanny sense of what would be likely to improve the quality of this or that type of steel. So he would advise adding to the alloy a trace more of copper or carbon, or he would suggest that the melt should be cooled a little more slowly. His was the real craftsman's approach to his work. But there was no real science in it, and as a result there were serious limitations to the progress that could be made. As the Oxford *History of Technology* puts it:

. . . the empirical element remained large, progress was achieved rather through the accumulated experience of craftsmen, the enterprise of management and the skill of individual designers, than through scientific insight . . . even the internal combustion engine and the [early stages of the] aeroplane owed more to creative empiricism and to persistent trial-and-error than to the availability of scientific theory.

How different all this is today! If you would enter the field of metals you must understand how X-ray diffraction will show you the arrangement of the atoms, you must be prepared to study the development of internal dislocations, and the storing of energy as a result of work-hardening; you will speak of the electron-atom concentration, and of the shape of the Fermi surface near the Brillouin zones. Yet none of these items is directly observable, and my old family friend in the Midlands (if he were still alive) would have no clue to the understanding of any of this sort of thing. In any discussion of future research policy he would be entirely out of his depth. For technology now depends on science.

Let me elaborate this in terms of my own family history. For several generations on my mother's side my forebears belonged to a family of inventors. I can produce early patents which my grandfather, great-grandfather and great-great-grandfather managed to obtain. The first automatic potato-peeling machine was designed by one of these gentlemen, and a modification in the shape of the screw (i.e. the propeller) of a boat was another. For these inventions the Lamb and Hancock families were quite well known, and I have several medals which were awarded to one or other member for inventions in the period 1850-1900. Now, not one single member of that family knew anything whatever about science. None had got a degree, or been to a university. But they were people with very considerable native ability, and a flair for thinking of something new. By the standards of the time they were successful inventors, though none of them ever made much money out of their inventions, and most of them were as poor as church mice! But they liked what they did.

This situation was typical of inventions almost up to the First World War. It was the age of the interested amateur. This can easily be seen if we ask about the status of those men who obtained patents. In Britain, for example, in the period to 1860, there were seventy-four patentees claiming to have devised a machine for producing perpetual motion. They included 'a Prince, a Baronet, two Counts, a Knight, a General, a Groom of the Privy Chamber, a D.D., two Doctors of Medicine, two Surgeons, a B.A., ten Gentlemen, four Merchants, ten Engineers, three Civil Engineers, an Architect, a Surveyor, a Contractor, a Manufacturer, a Brewer, a Millwright, a Miller, five Machinists, a Carpenter, a Draftsman, a Jeweller, a Watchmaker, a Confectioner, a Shoemaker, a Customs-house Official, with nine persons and seven foreigners undescribed.' It is a quaint list, at which we may not unreasonably smile, but the variety of occupation and profession represented shows that inventions, and their result in technology, were still largely the responsibility of the non-professional, the amateur.

Such a situation is no longer possible, except in a few isolated pockets where, for one reason or another, industries pay relatively little attention to what the scientists can say. When this happens, it is not difficult to detect deficiencies in the final product. Let me illustrate this by reference to a situation which existed twenty years ago in Dundee. Dundee is the centre of the jute industry in Britain, and jute is used as a basis of linoleum and, more significantly, of sandbags. Everyone who remembers the early years of World War II will recall the way in which we all filled sandbags and built them up into walls as a protection against damage from bomb and blast. But the lifetime of these sandbags often seemed to be a mere fortnight, because of weakness or rot. This could have been altered. For jute is a fibre, and a good deal of fundamental research work had been done by university and other scientists on the strengthening of fibres, either natural or artificial, by a process of cross-linking, so that one molecular chain was joined to another somewhat like the way that the two sides of a ladder are joined by the cross-linking rungs. In rubber this whole process was well known under the the label vulcanization. One or two of us tried to encourage the jute industry to study the application of these principles to jute. But in all the jute industry, where—if I remember rightly—several million sandbags were being made every month, we failed to get one single manufacturer who would be prepared to sponsor research into this process. Here was one of those pockets of resistance, though now (I believe) mercifully done away. A few others, of course, still remain, surviving outposts of an approach to technology which is doomed. The only policy now is to bring the scientist and the inventor together. The scientist-turned-inventor-turned-engineer holds the keys of the future. There is no hope whatever for my children if they follow the example of their great-grandparents!

Yet this complete change in industrial technology is relatively recent; and most certainly belongs to our second revolution. The largest chemical firm in the

U.S.A. is the firm of du Pont. And when, in the early 1940's it became a matter of life and death that huge plant should be erected to enrich the uranium for the first atomic bomb, and to convert large amounts of it to plutonium for the second, it was natural that General Groves, who was in charge of the planning, should approach this firm to enlist their help. After a fortnight to think things over, their Vice-President Dr Charles Stine is reported to have said: 'du Pont is the only company that can do the task. We must do it, even though it may break the Company.' In the light of their subsequent successful carrying through of this colossal task, it is instructive to remember that this firm had been in existence for a complete century, before, in 1902, they started their first formal research venture! Yet when I visited one of their laboratories a few years ago, I saw more nuclear-magnetic-resonance instruments in one single building than existed at that time in all the universities in Britain.

Some figures of the amount of money spent by industry on research will illustrate this very clearly. In 1935 the United States spent 200 million dollars on research. In 1953 the figure had jumped to 5,370 million dollars—and of this huge sum 72 per cent was expended on industrial research laboratories, 18 per cent on State laboratories, and 9 per cent on university laboratories. As for the money spent by industry, there is a close relation between this and its age. If an industry is more than about sixty years old the proportion of its turnover which is spent on developing the scientific side by research and experiment is usually small (though now often increasing). But if the industry has been founded within the last thirty years, the proportion is much bigger. Large concerns frequently allocate more than 5 per cent of their total budget on research, using the best scientists who are available. Science and industry are thereby linked so closely that, for example, the largest purely professional scientific society in the world is the American Chemical Society, and at the same time by far the greater number of its members are in industry.

The inventor can do very little nowadays without the resources which science has provided for him. Since in a later chapter we shall have to consider the relation of science and technology to war, it may be opportune to refer to the way in which the character of war—and sometimes the eventual victor—has been determined by technology. Sir Alexander Fleck, the Chairman of I.C.I. Ltd., has written of how

the Macedonian Phalanx and the Roman legion, the bowmen of England and Cromwell's Ironsides, each formed a decisive contribution to the technology of warfare, but in the American Civil War (during the first industrial revolution, in the mid-nineteenth century) for the first time, the technological resources of a whole nation were ultimately mobilized to overwhelm an opponent. There was mass-production of weapons and ammunition, of uniforms and boots; canned food was supplied to armies transported for the first time by rail. In a famous dispatch to Lincoln in 1862, John Ericsson, who had designed the floating armoured battery *Monitor*, wrote: 'The time has come, Mr President, when our cause will have to be sustained not by numbers, but by superior weapons. By a proper application of mechanical devices alone will you be able with absolute certainty to destroy the enemies of the Union.'

This is certainly impressive. But we have only to compare this situation with that found in the last two world wars to realize how much more profoundly the combination of scientist and technologist has been able to influence things. We say, with justification, that the First World War was won by the chemists, with their developments of poison gas and high-explosives; and that the Second World War was won by the physicists, with the development of radar, aeroplanes, and atomic power. None of all this list of discoveries could have been made without very considerable fundamental scientific knowledge.

Let us pursue one of these items a little farther, for in so doing we shall be able more clearly to see the intimate relationship between science and technology. Let us ask about the development of nuclear power for atomic bombs or for peaceful purposes such as at Calder Hall or Winfrith Heath. The taming of the atom was not someone's bright idea, when they were resting in a hammock one Sunday afternoon! To trace its history we must go back to 1915, when Rutherford first began to show that an atom had a nucleus, and that in radioactivity this nucleus could split; we must next go to 1931 when in the Cavendish Laboratory at Cambridge, Chadwick discovered the neutron. (This was a purely academic exercise, if such language may be allowed.) Then we move to 1939 when it was first recognized, by Hahn, Meitner, and others, that when a uranium atom splits, it divides into two nearly equal parts, and some neutrons are given off at the same moment. All this information is to be infused with the purely theoretical ideas of an Einstein concerning the relation $E = mc^2$ between mass and energy, and with the even more abstract ideas of a French theoretical physicist de Broglie suggesting that when tiny particles are moving they behave rather like waves as well as particles. Who would have supposed that all this was a necessary preliminary to the development of nuclear power? Yet not one single item in this list could be dispensed with. In a very real sense the technology of today is based on science. It is this which gives it its present power; it is this which also takes it out of the hands of ordinary people.

This is leading me to the second comment that I wish to make on the influence of our second industrial revolution. The ordinary person is puzzled by it. This is because, in the combination of science and technology, he cannot understand what is happening. Furthermore his puzzlement is made all the worse on account of the speed with which this combination achieves results. It is not always appreciated quite how fast science now progresses. In the old days—which means, once again, up to the middle, or even the end, of the nineteenth century!—things happened so slowly that an intelligent person could keep up with them. Scientists themselves— as a peculiar species of human being—were almost unknown: even the word 'scientist' dates only from 1841, in the year when William Whewell, at that time Master of Trinity, became President of the British Association, and coined the word because he wanted a label to identify the professional who had recently come into existence, and for whom the title of natural philosopher seemed not quite appropriate—even though in Scotland a university physicist is still described in this way! In the lifetime of an ordinary person only two or three major scientific developments took place. For example, there were 250 years between the early experiments on magnetism by Gilbert and others to the rounding-off of the theory of electricity and magnetism by James Clerk Maxwell in the

1870's. But as we come to more modern days the time interval decreases. It was fifty years from Michael Faraday's early experiments at the Royal Institution on the movement of a wire carrying a current in the presence of a magnetic field to its commercial exploitation in electric dynamos and motors. It was twenty-five years —notice how the time-scale is abbreviated—from Becquerel's discovery of X-rays until the time when they were being pretty widely used in medical practice. It was only eleven years from the discovery of nuclear fission to the first self-sustained nuclear pile. Seven years passed between the recognition that an atomic bomb was theoretically possible and the dropping of the first two such bombs. Only three years elapsed from the discovery (which, incidentally, was made in an industrial laboratory) that the wireless and electronics industry could be completely transformed by the replacement of ordinary filament valves by transistors, to their worldwide commercial production and sale. In one single year now, approximately one hundred thousand completed pieces of original research in chemistry are published in the technical and scientific press, and twenty thousand chemical patents are granted: probably a million new scientific facts are discovered every year. The situation is almost frightening in its acceleration. Nor does there seem at present to be any slackening in the pace of discovery. If it is said that these million new facts are chiefly scientific and not technological, I shall point to the close link between science and technology, which I have previously claimed to be one of the most characteristic features of today, and shall quote some words of Thomas S. Kuhn in a book describing the Copernican Revolution: 'Every fundamental innovation in a scientific speciality inevitably transforms neighbouring sciences, and, more slowly, the worlds of the philosopher and the educated layman.' He might well have added that after the educated layman there comes the uneducated one, who experiences the changes but without understanding them.

I would like to refer specifically to one region where the puzzlement of the ordinary man shows itself in the presence of a serious cultural loss. This could be called the loss of tradition. It can be traced without any hesitation to the ignorance of people in the face of great and rapidly changing ways of life. The age in which we are living is uniquely characterized by the loss of traditions. And this, as Michael Foster has put it in an essay on tradition, is one of the most important things about it, marking it off from all previous ages in which men have lived. Think for a moment of some of our characteristically British traditional activities, and see how in every case the interpolation of technology has destroyed them in their strict traditional sense. Away in the Hebrides the islanders sang their sad and lonely songs— they sang them freely, as a bird sings in the unfolding dawn. They did not learn them, they were handed down. But Kennedy Fraser came with his recording machines: the 'Songs of the Hebrides' were killed, to be replaced by properly scored printed music and a few dozen gramophone records. Henceforth all men everywhere could 'learn' these haunting melodies; they had ceased to be traditional. It was just the same with the English folk dances. Here in Headington where I live, they have danced the Morris dances from time immemorial, with exuberant gladness and the freshness of green grass upon their clothes. But Cecil Sharp has changed all that; the steps are fully catalogued, and sophisticated university students on May morning dance around the streets of Oxford to show that these human responses are no longer traditional. So also in building. The architectural history of Oxford, as of any ancient city, shows a succession of architectural styles. Most of the building was done by people who lived within a particular tradition, who did not ask themselves what style they should adopt for any new building, but who just built, naturally and without artifice. As Michael Foster puts it, 'they were within a style, and carried it out'. But now, as at Oxford where the university is shortly to develop a large new area known as the Keble Triangle, we are no longer in a tradition, and furious debates take place to decide whether we should build in Gothic, Renaissance, Classical, modern Danish or other style. It is because of the consciousness of change, and the greater freedom presented to us by scientific technology, that this puzzlement arises. The significance of all this, for a tribal society such as the African, is all too clear. In Rhodesia and in Ghana and in Sierra Leone we are witnessing the break-up of a traditional culture pattern in a perilously short time interval. Of course there are good aspects of this, as well as dangerous or bad ones, and I shall have something to say about them in a later chapter.

But we ourselves are no less subject to this change. Let Michael Foster speak of his choice of a toothpaste.

In a sense science and tradition are opposites. On the tube of toothpaste which I normally use is written 'a scientific dental cream'. What does it mean when a manufacturer puts on the dental cream that it is 'scientific'? It means it has not been made by the carrying out of traditional processes

learned from his father, and handed down from his fore-
fathers. It has not been done traditionally, but in a different
way—a scientific way, which means he has broken with
tradition, and is applying this other non-traditional method.

In some respects it is the loss of tradition, in the wide
sense in which I have been using this phrase, which lies
at the core of nearly all the problems, of conduct, of
ethics and morals, of food and population, of education
and of power, whose discussion will occupy the remaining
chapters of this book. The Christian cannot properly
remain unmoved by these influences, recognized and
unrecognized. And—though this is not by any means
always realized—neither can the scientist himself. But
that is to be our concern in our next chapter. For the
present it will be sufficient if we begin to glimpse the
astonishing scale along which our second industrial
revolution is proceeding, and the unexampled speed with
which its influences stretch out; and if we can identify
these with the newly-established link between science
and modern technology; and are thereby prepared to
interpret the malaise of modern man. It is not until we
have seen all this that we have any right to confront him
with the Christian gospel, or condemn him for what
seem to us the failings of his way of life.

CHAPTER TWO

Moral Responsibility of Scientists

THERE IS A popular view that the scientist is under no obligation to consider the uses to which his work may be put, and is therefore a particularly dangerous member of society. Those of us who are ourselves professional scientists know only too well that in the public estimation we tend to be either the High Priests of the New Order, or the whipping-boy who must share the blame for all those evils, such as the hydrogen bomb, which cloud the future. Now if science and technology are to play so great a part in shaping the future of the human race as we saw to be the case in the last chapter, it immediately becomes a matter of the gravest importance whether scientists do or do not acknowledge their responsibilities. Is it 'science for science's sake', without reference to public safety or concern? Is it the case, in the words which the nuclear physicist J. R. Oppenheimer used when testifying before the United States Congressional Committee on loyalty, that if a project is 'technically sweet'', scientists can always be found who are prepared to go ahead with it? This particular project was the development of the H-bomb, but the question could be asked about almost any other scientific discovery of importance. It was Rabelais who said *'Science sans conscience n'est que ruine de l'âme'*. Science without conscience is quite clearly dangerous: but what about scientists?

It is perfectly obvious to anyone with knowledge of

modern government research groups, especially those involved in matters of defence, that the facilities provided are usually far better and attractive than those which are available in pure research in universities. In the early days after the war, the equipment to be seen at Harwell was so munificent as to make a university physicist or chemist blush. And at the time of writing this paragraph, the Atomic Weapons Research Establishment at Aldermaston is the only place in Britain where there may be found one of the huge I.B.M. electronic computers, so big that even its rental charge is of the order of a quarter of a million pounds per year. In the U.S.A. there are something like fifty of these machines, nearly all of which are either in navy, ordnance or air force hands, or in the possession of larger aircraft companies, often depending on government funds for the financing of their major research products. There is no denying that the opportunity of enjoying access to the best types of equipment does constitute a tremendous attraction to a scientist, and occasionally lulls him into a state of torpor so far as the application of his work is concerned. I believe that we should learn to recognize this and deal gently with such people.

But quite apart from the lure of better equipment, there is the matter of principle. Here, as we shall see, opinion is divided. For example, not all of us would sign away our responsibilities so completely as the writer of a letter to *The Listener*, who states, following a talk on the responsibility of scientists:

My scientific training and experience were obtained essentially at the expense of the State, and it is therefore reasonable that the State should use them in whatever manner it considers to be most valuable. . . .

In Christian times there was a well-known quotation which some people may still remember: 'Render unto Caesar the things that are Caesar's, and unto God the things that are God's.' My scientific ability, such as it is, is Caesar's, and to him I render it, confident that my personal behaviour in the twentieth-century jungle is for God to judge.

The writer of that letter was in the Government Scientific Service. But, quite apart from his reference to the 'well-known quotation' that belonged to 'Christian times', it is hard to believe that he realizes what the Christian judgement on such matters would be. It was a coin, the token of man's way of changing goods and chattels from hand to hand, that Jesus used to illustrate the possessions of Caesar. Very few of us would feel happy at including our scientific ability in this category. As the mathematician Jacobi said to Fourier, when he was being reproached for not spending enough time on the solution of certain problems in the conduction of heat, we do our science 'for the honour of the human mind'. It may conceivably be true of the professional soldier, in the words of the Duke of Wellington, 'I have ate of the King's salt, and consider myself bound to go where I am sent, and do as I am ordered' (though such a plea was not accepted as adequate in the trial of Nazi war criminals at Nuremberg), but man's creative spirit, his winning of knowledge by experiment, his growing power to modify or control his environment—these cannot be bought and sold in the market of government, of industry or of politics.

What may be called the policy of non-involvement is really never able to be practised, and we delude ourselves if we think that it can. Our work has its influences however much we try to blind ourselves to them. The film producer who, in a recent television show, concerned with the dangers arising out of too much physical violence in certain types of modern film, blandly exclaimed, 'We're in the entertainment business; it isn't *our* job to shape human lives', was uttering a disclaimer that possessed no validity at all. Whether he knew it or not, he *was* shaping human lives. One of the most sinister aspects of the McCarthy era in American politics of 1950-5, was the claim that 'scientists should be on tap, not on top'. It was because very few scientists in America were prepared to think of themselves as 'on tap', and not because they all wanted places in the limelight 'on top', that it was among the scientists that there grew up the most implacable hatred and distrust of this misguided man.

The fact is that scientists, as such, are much like ordinary people. As a result, their conduct during the centuries of the growth of science has been varied. But during the last twenty years, as a consequence of the greater danger in modern weapons, their opinions have been becoming much more definite and incisive. It may therefore be worth while to study briefly the ways in which scientists have dealt with their conscience, not just in the twentieth century, but in the centuries before. Since, until very recently, the most important moral problems that confronted the scientist were connected with the use of his discoveries in war, nearly all the examples of which we have records relate to war, rather than industry or commerce.

In a recent study of alchemy, Sherwood Taylor has shown how the early alchemists were concerned about the use to which their work might be put if it fell into the wrong hands.

Alchemy was certainly intended to be useful. . . . But the alchemist never proposes the *public* use of such things, the disclosing of his knowledge for the benefit of man. . . . Any disclosure of the alchemical secret was felt to be profoundly wrong, and likely to bring immediate punishment from on high. The reason generally given for such secrecy was the probable abuse by wicked men of the power that the alchemical secret would give. . . . The alchemists, indeed, felt a strong moral responsibility for the result of their work.

Dr Taylor goes on to point out that this responsibility is not so universally accepted in the twentieth century.

The material aim of the alchemists, the transmutation of metals, has now been realized by science and the alchemical vessel is the uranium pile. Its success has had precisely the result that the alchemists feared and guarded against, the placing of gigantic power in the hands of those who have not been fitted by spiritual training to receive it.

In a moment we shall have to ask further questions about the control of power. For the moment let us remember that with the coming of the Renaissance scientific knowledge, like other knowledge, became public property. Yet the scientist's conscience was never at ease. It may be true that people like Leonardo da Vinci, at the end of the fifteenth century, could write a letter to the Duke of Milan asking for employment, and quote in support of his application no less than ten qualifications, nine of which related to his ability as a military engineer: but as for his design of a submarine he said:

This I do not . . . divulge on account of the evil nature of men, who would practise assassinations at the bottom of the seas, by breaking the ships in their lowest parts and sinking them together with the crews who are in them.

So also

Napier (the inventor of logarithms) refused to divulge the
nature of a weapon he had developed; Boyle (one of the
founder members of the Royal Society) refused to publish
the ingredients of some poisons and a means of making ink
invisible, as being 'mischievous'. He also subsidized a Dr
Kuffler on constructive projects in order to keep him from
developing 'dreadful and destroying inventions'. The Italian
scientist Tartaglia (in the middle of the sixteenth century)
became fascinated with projectile theory but his sense of
guilt made him burn up everything he had written on the
subject.[1]

When he was withholding publication of some of his
results on the sighting and aiming of firearms, he wrote:

It had seemed to me that it was a thing blameworthy,
shameful and barbarous, worthy of severe punishment
before God and man, to wish to bring to perfection an act
damageable to one's neighbour and destructive to the human
race.

The difficulties in which a scientist may find himself when
faced with possible destruction of his country by enemies
—difficulties enormously more involved now than then
—ultimately proved too much for Tartaglia's restraint.
For when the Turks later invaded Italy, he felt prompted
to come to the aid of Christendom, rewrote his works and
published them.

A hundred years after the same problem arises in
England, and in *Brewster's Encyclopedia* there is the
story of the horror with which Sir Isaac Newton greeted
the announcement by a certain Professor Gregory of

[1] This, and the earlier quotation from Sherwood Taylor, are taken
from a paper by O. T. Benfey, *Bulletin of Atomic Scientists, 12* (1956),
p. 177, by permission.

Oxford that the latter's father had completed the model of an invention for making artillery more destructive.

Sir Isaac was much displeased with it, saying that if it tended as much to the preservation of mankind as to their destruction, the inventor would have deserved a great reward; but as it was contrived solely for destruction, and would soon be known to the enemy, he rather deserved to be punished, and urged the Professor very strongly to destroy it, and if possible to suppress the invention.

It is interesting to recall that a hundred years ago, during the Crimean War, the British Government consulted Michael Faraday with regard to the feasibility of using poison gas in an attack. Faraday replied that it was entirely feasible, but it was inhuman, and, for himself, he would have nothing to do with it. It may well be claimed that with the coming of the two industrial revolutions, the conditions of life have so far changed that these early judgements are no longer relevant. I have described them, nevertheless, because I believe we ought to recognize that the scientist is a human being, tortured by the same conflicting claims as the rest of us and not necessarily enjoying any greater wisdom; at no time has he made that solemn pact with the devil that many people erroneously suppose. Indeed it is possible to go farther than this, and I would like to suggest that at the present time there is no similar-sized professional group which has anything like the same degree of concern for social responsibility as the scientific group. I do not mean by this that as a group they properly understand the ultimately religious basis on which their concern rests; for often they go so far as to misunderstand it. But I am very anxious to show how widespread is their concern, and later I shall suggest that the Christian community is here presented with a considerable opportunity.

First let me draw attention to the astonishing number of groups of scientists who have banded themselves together to make their influence greater. I am thinking amongst many others of the Society for Freedom in Science, the Society for Social Responsibility in Science, the Atomic Scientists Association, the new Section of the British Association devoted to social responsibility, Science for Peace, and, most recently, the Pugwash Conferences. This great movement is something unique to our time. And so also is the outspoken way in which many of the world's leading scientists have spoken. Thus, Bertrand Russell in a speech to scientists at a meeting called by the Campaign for Nuclear Disarmament in 1959:

Science, ever since it first existed, has had important effects in matters that lie outside the purview of pure science. Men of science have differed as to their responsibility for such effects. Some have said that the function of the scientist in society is to supply knowledge, and that he need not concern himself with the use to which this knowledge is put. I do not think that this view is tenable, especially in our age. The scientist is also a citizen, and citizens who have any special skill have a public duty to see, as far as they can, that their skill is utilized in accordance with the public interest.

This feeling is worldwide. In America, for example, E. U. Condon, one of the leaders in atomic research:

Whether scientific knowledge is used for good or evil purposes is a matter that is not part of science itself, but it is a matter of the deepest concern to scientists who are human beings having the same moral responsibilities and the same responsibilities as citizens as have other people. Therefore, we cannot escape the necessity of giving thought and effort to the conditions under which science and scientists make their contribution to the world's progress.

And Norbert Wiener, the founder of the science of cybernetics, on which the remote control of all rockets and long-range missiles is based: 'I do not expect to publish any future work of mine which may do damage in the hands of irresponsible militarists.' In Germany in April 1947, at the time when it was first being proposed that the Bundeswehr should be armed with atomic weapons, there was an immediate response by eighteen of her most famous scientists, including no less than five Nobel prizewinners, who wrote a public letter to the Federal Chancellor utterly refusing to take any part in such work. This was immediately endorsed and carried further by a group of Quaker professional scientists in Britain. And, a year later, the 3000-member Union of German Societies for Physics meeting in Essen (West Germany) issued a document opposing research in atomic weapons; they reminded scientists that the 'progressive development of nuclear weapons and other means of mass destruction of every kind was generally impossible without the active co-operation of physicists' and they made plans to help scientists who lost their jobs because of a refusal to work on atomic weapons.

Perhaps more surprising than all this was the result of a questionnaire sent out in September 1958 to ninety-two technical and trade magazines in the U.S.A. asking the editors of these journals about their policy in regard

to the publication of articles discussing the social
responsibility of scientists and engineers. Most people
would have expected the pages of these technical journals
to be closed to writing of this kind; as the editor of one
of them replied: 'No . . . the engineer, in our book, is a
devoted man whose sole aim is to help his plant produce
more, and thus enrich the standard of living for mankind.' But the astonishing situation revealed by the
first forty-nine replies to the questionnaire was that no
less than thirty said that, with certain qualifications,
they thought such discussions had a place in their
journal, and only nineteen said that they had not.

Yet all this pales before some of the more recent
documents. In January 1958 Professor Linus Pauling of
California presented to Mr Dag Hammarskjold, the
Secretary-General of the United Nations, a petition
signed by no less than 9235 scientists, from almost every
country in the world (forty-four in all), including ninety-
five Fellows of our Royal Society and 216 Members and
Correspondents of the Academy of Sciences of the
U.S.S.R. In the words of this petition—

We, the scientists whose names are signed below, urge that
an international agreement to stop the testing of nuclear
bombs be made now. . . .

We have in common with our fellow men a deep concern for
the welfare of all human beings. As scientists we have
knowledge of the dangers involved and therefore a special
responsibility to make those dangers known. We deem it
imperative that immediate action be taken to effect an
international agreement to stop the testing of all nuclear
weapons.[2]

[2] A full account is in Linus Pauling's book, *No More War* (Gollancz,
1958).

This growing international concern among scientists is impressive. But this is not the only example. In January 1957 the American Association for the Advancement of Science adopted a report, referred to as the Pigman Report, emphasizing the need for scientists to concern themselves more closely with social action, since 'the determination that scientific knowledge is to be used for human good, or for purposes of destruction is in the control of social agencies . . . here scientists can play a decisive role'. Since the A.A.A.S. numbers two million members among its affiliated groups, this step, somewhat reluctantly taken, and a complete reversal of a traditional policy of isolationism, represents a very significant and far-reaching change in American thought. It is a recognition, now nearly universal among the physical sciences, that in the words of Professor M. L. Oliphant 'the bomb blew to pieces the world of disinterested science'. It is not surprising that these developments should have been followed by the Pugwash Conferences, of which three have so far been held. These conferences, due in the first place to a letter issued in July 1955 by Einstein, Bertrand Russell, and nine other scientists and calling for an international meeting of scientists to assess some of the dangers in which the world stood in respect of nuclear bombs, have brought together the chief scientists of all the major countries. They have met, in freedom and without restraint; they have reached surprisingly great agreement. The immense prestige of those attending has given an authority which is without precedent[3] to the documents which they have issued, and (in the case of the second conference) sent to the Heads of State of fifteen different

[3] An account is given in *The New Scientist* (9th October, 1958).

countries. It is certainly significant when leading American, British, Japanese, and Russian scientists can sign a single document including these words:

We believe it to be a responsibility of scientists in all countries to contribute to the education of the peoples by spreading among them a wide understanding of the dangers and potentialities offered by the unprecedented growth of science. We appeal to our colleagues everywhere to contribute to this effort.

In view of all this mutual concern, it should come as no surprise that in all sections of science, both biological and physical, discussions are proceeding to see whether some sort of Hippocratic Oath could be devised which would provide a rallying ground for the whole scientific community. I have two or three such proposals in front of me now, as I write. In the Hippocratic oaths to which doctors of nearly every country subscribe, there is a definite promise to accept some degree of responsibility for the welfare of all men, everywhere; and not to misuse the art of healing. ('In purity and holiness will I guard my art.') I am by no means sure that such an oath can ever be more binding than the conscience of the man who solemnly swears to it: which is equivalent to saying that right conduct, for scientists and doctors no less than for other people, begins in the hearts and minds, and not in convention. But the mood of scientific thought at the moment is very different from what it was. If it were not so, such talk as this would never arise.

I have been describing the growing sense of responsibility among scientists, and their concern about the use of science and technology, but I can almost hear objectors protesting that at the one most significant single moment of history in the last nineteen hundred years scientists were powerless to prevent a calamity whose magnitude now seems to grow with the years. I refer to the dropping of the first two atomic bombs on Japan in 1945. Before concluding this chapter it is desirable that the facts regarding this situation should be made clear. For they are not so widely known as they should be.

In the first place the scientists working on the atomic bomb were deeply troubled. In Robert Jungk's book which gives an account of the bomb right from its first proposal by Einstein, the chapter on the development of the H-bomb correctly carries the heading 'Conflict of Conscience'. At the end of his life, Einstein himself publicly stated that he did wrong in advising the American President to go ahead with the scheme: Oppenheimer wrote later that in all this ghastly business, the physicist had sinned; and Max Born said that 'what we are concerned with is collective guilt'.

The scientists at Los Alamos and Chicago were troubled, but they were not unanimous. It was a curiously poignant responsibility that they carried, for they—and they alone—knew what was being built in the 'Met. Lab.' during the fateful early months of 1945. They could not publicly debate policy or even show a public interest, since this would have conceivably led to a dangerous leakage of information. But, as A. H. Compton's autobiography *Atomic Quest* shows very clearly, they were incessantly debating with each other the likely future once the war was ended, and nuclear knowledge was available for any country; and they argued vehemently as to the rightness or wrongness of dropping an atomic bomb on the cities of Japan, or somewhere else, where it could be a sign of what would ultimately happen to Japan if she did not surrender. One of their number, Dr Leo Szilard, wrote a memorandum in March of 1945 and sent it to President Roosevelt. This argued strongly in favour of an immediate international control of nuclear weapons and forecast with almost uncanny prescience the dangers—political, international, and social—that the world would not be able to avoid without such control. President Roosevelt died before the memorandum reached him, though six weeks before the first New Mexico test, Dr Szilard did have the opportunity of a personal interview with the White House representative Mr James F. Byrnes. Another memorandum, the Franck Report, was sent to the Secretary of War in June 1945, a month before the test. It was prepared by seven of the leading scientists on the project, and warned against actual use of the bomb. 'We believe', it said, 'that these considerations make the use of nuclear bombs for an earlier unannounced attack against Japan inadvisable. If the United States were to be the first to release this new means of indiscriminate destruction on mankind, she would sacrifice public support throughout the world, precipitate the race for armaments, and prejudice the possibility of reaching an international agreement on the future control of such weapons.'

In a secret poll which was carried out in Chicago four days before the first experimental test in New Mexico, only 15 per cent of the scientists voted to use atomic bombs 'in the manner that is from the military point of view most effective in bringing about prompt Japanese surrender at minimum human cost to our armed forces'. The other 85 per cent may have been divided on precisely what course they did advise, but they were not

prepared to commit all their responsibility into the
hands of other people. In the event, of course, their views
were not accepted; President Truman has explicitly
stated that the decision to use the bomb was fully and
entirely his. More recently Sir John Cockcroft has
reported his own opinion: 'If, then, we can sum up the
position of British and Allied scientists in this period, I
would claim that they have acted with a full sense of
their responsibility to their country and to world
civilization.'

The tragedy of the American situation is that the 85
per cent were right; but they lacked the full courage of
their convictions.[4]

In this chapter I have tried to gather enough material,
supported by direct quotation, to show that scientists
have felt varying degrees of responsibility for their work;
and that, in the years since the last war, this sense of
responsibility has grown into a world movement.
Perhaps, before closing the chapter, I may be allowed to
offer some comments from the point of view of a
Christian.

Scientists, like other men, have to live, and they
prefer to do the things that interest them. They suffer
from the same temptation as others to rationalize the
doing of what they want to do, particularly if their
living depends upon it. But even in early days they have
felt unhappy twinges of conscience. Yet when science
and technology joined together, and the results were as
devastating as they now most evidently are, they revolt
from the evil that they see. But because their spiritual
beliefs are so different, and the spiritual traditions of

[4] The best account of this episode is by Alice K. Smith, in the *Bulletin
of the Atomic Scientists* (October 1958).

their separate countries differ also, there is agreement only on the negative aspects of this responsibility. For agreement on a positive programme is only possible among people who share the same inner convictions out of which action grows. What is needed, if this present mood is not to fade and dissipate itself, is a common commanding conviction. Because I believe that the Christian faith provides this conviction, I am desperately anxious that we shall understand the dilemma in which the scientist now stands, and, instead of blaming him for opening Pandora's Box and releasing every conceivable evil upon an innocent world, recognize our share of the blame in not providing the background of thought within which he can do his own thinking; we must seek a way of showing him that we share his concern, and can help him to place it in its proper context—which is nothing other than the Kingdom of God.

CHAPTER THREE

Relation to the Christian Faith—Some General Principles

IT IS TIME to see where our arguments have so far led us. In the first chapter I described the rise of technology in the first industrial revolution, and its potent link with science in the second. In the curiously exciting and rapidly changing environment that we all share, it was natural that tradition should cease to be so significant, and that the younger generation should find themselves confronted with problems for which the wisdom of their fathers provided little guidance. In the second chapter I described the response which the scientists and technicians themselves have given. It was a mixed story, of good resolve tempered all too often by personal considerations and a failure to respond at a sufficiently deep level. But it showed that the scientists and technicians most certainly do not deserve the opprobrium which they have sometimes received.

This brings us to the point where we must consider the response of the non-scientist, and the relation of those kaleidoscopic changes which I have described to our Christian faith. This story, like the one before, will be found to be mixed.

In the first place we have come to see that our future depends upon a full development of technology. For example, in the United States one of the President's Advisory Committees reports that 'science is a necessary element in national survival'. In Communist countries the convention of having widely-publicized five-year plans for industry is so well established that we accept it without recognizing its witness to the conviction that salvation lies in science and technology, rather than in any of the other great movements of the human spirit. Even the designs on the postage stamps of most such countries, with their emphasis on cranes, and factories, and machines, bear silent confirmation of this view. The same is true among ourselves. Just before he left Birmingham University to return to Australia, Professor Oliphant asserted in a broadcast that 'our modern civilization is founded on technology, and technology on science'. Even in the West we should most of us grant a grudging assent to this view. But I want to understand why it is necessary to use that adjective 'grudging'. Why, in fact, are Christians so lethargic and hesitant in their approach to all things technological?

There can be little doubt but that their approach really is of this kind. You will look almost in vain for any book published by the many religious presses in this country, which dares to write the word 'technology' into its title. Church Guild meetings will discuss literary topics, social service topics, religious topics; but who has heard of their discussing technological issues? Would it not be fair to say that to many otherwise excellent Christians even the word 'technology' has a slightly dirty connotation, with an undertone of 'not being quite nice'? Fifty years or more ago, in the latter days of the first industrial revolution, this might have been linked with the fact that we are a predominantly middle-class grouping, where the black coat is more frequent than the dungarees. But such an excuse is less valid today, since in the second industrial revolution the scientist and the technologist have become blood brethren. In the words of Lord Adrian: 'Class distinctions . . . have been greatly weakened, and there is no longer any stigma attached to an idea or a technique that was born and bred in a workshop rather than in a university.' The real reasons for the Christian's equivocal attitude are deeper than this. They are compounded of (*a*) suspicion, (*b*) ignorance, and (*c*) misunderstanding. The suspicion is directed against the technologist who seems to have too great a power for good or evil; the ignorance arises from not sufficiently knowing the nature of science and technology: the misunderstanding—in some ways the worst of all—is misunderstanding of our own Christian doctrine of creation, leading to false ideas about materialism. We must deal with each of these in turn.

First there is suspicion. We have seen enormous changes taking place in our own lifetime. We know that it is the fruit of technology which has enriched our lives, and so there must be something magical, almost witch-like, about it. We fear it, despite its bounty. *Timeo Danaos, et dona ferentis.* Science is our fairy godmother since all the items from washing-machines to television sets which adorn our modern houses are manifestly the offspring of scientific knowledge. Yet it is sinister, because not only washing-machines, but also atomic weapons, nerve gases and other horrors are its children. Would it be too much of an exaggeration to transcribe this often unexpressed suspicion as follows?

I do not understand the antics of the medicine man: so like the other members of my tribe, I fear him. I do not understand the strange language of the scientists, when they speak of electrons or of fields of force. So I fear them too. It is different with the politician. I can keep some sort of watch on his manœuvres, because he speaks the queen's English, and his ways are not so different from mine. But the scientist speaks a language that I do not understand, and the technologist plays with forces too mysterious for me. They are dangerous: I don't know what they will do next; I had better be suspicious of them.

A year or so ago the American University of Purdue conducted a large-scale survey of career preferences among a group which we should call sixth-form boys and girls. This survey included all of the forty-eight States at that time in the U.S.A. It also comprised town and rural areas. Among several other questions typical of an American Gallup poll, the 15,000 boys and girls were asked to make some comments on a list of possible occupations. Would they rather be a doctor, a teacher, a storekeeper, an atomic scientist? There were about twenty possible occupations. But the astonishing result was that in every State, among rich and poor, rural and urban, the profession of atomic scientist came bottom. And even worse—thirty per cent believed that one cannot raise a normal family and be a scientist at the same time, twenty-seven per cent thought that scientists were willing to sacrifice the welfare of others to further their own interests, twenty-eight per cent did not believe that scientists have time to enjoy life, twenty-five per cent thought that scientists as a group were more than a little bit 'odd', fourteen per cent thought that there is something 'evil' about scientists, and nine per cent believed that it was not possible for a scientist to be honest. The Purdue report comments on these findings as follows:

Dstc

If students feel that scientific occupations have no dignity or
that scientists are usually evil men, or that only geniuses are
competent scientists, they are less likely to consider technical
education as occupational preparation. There is some
evidence that such attitudes exist in the general population
and not just among high-school students. Some of these
adverse attitudes arise from anti-intellectualism, which is
often expressed as fear of 'eggheads'. Also some of these
negative attitudes may stem from the part which science
has been required to play in the development of weapons.

I have reason to believe that the situation in America is a
little better now than in 1956 when this report was issued:
and we must not read too much into one single survey.
But a good deal of the same attitude of mind remains,
both there and among ourselves. I am sure that this
equivocal attitude is one that we should set ourselves
both to understand and to restrain; and we shall need to
begin in our educational system. This is particularly
true for those of us who are Christians; for we know in
our own experience how closely juxtaposed are good and
evil. We know too that it is God's intention that His
children should grow up, not so much running away from
the evil as overcoming it with good. We at least should
be able to look squarely into the dangers with which we
must now learn to live. The existence of the danger is
no ground for an irrational response.

The second reason why the Christian often fails in his
attitude to science and technology is plain ignorance—
a belief that science has disproved the existence of God,
or made faith in Him incompatible with full mental
integrity; a barely concealed assumption that science,
by providing for our needs, has made God unnecessary;
a notion that technology is aesthetically unsatisfying and

ugly; or that it is without any moral excellence, humility or other grace. These are common enough beliefs among Christians. Yet not one of them is true. In the first place, science has never 'proved' anything; and this includes proving either the existence or non-existence of God. I have dealt with this situation in my little book, *Science and Christian Belief*,[5] and do not propose to say more here. But some of the other issues deserve a few comments.

There is a small group of which I was recently a member, which has been trying to list the questions that bother ordinary people, so that we may help to answer them. In the section on religion here is the first question that this group had to deal with. 'Once we crowded the churches to fight plague—now we dig drains; once we prayed for rain—now we seed clouds; once we prayed for plenty—now we use fertilizers and insecticides. Thus every scientific advance limits the area where God is supposed to operate. Doesn't this prove that we have outgrown religion?' This is the point of view widely held among scientific humanists and Communists, and well-illustrated in the little poem published by the Russian magazine *Krokodil* after the first sputnik went into orbit:

> *And here we have our Sputnik.*
> *No secret: the newborn planet*
> *Is modest about its size.*
> *But this symbol of intellect and light*
> *Is made by us, and not by the God*
> *Of the Old Testament.*

The best—and Christian—answer to such claims is the

[5] Fontana Books (Collins, 1959).

quiet reminder that all the scientific knowledge that men gain will fail to give them rules of conduct, and that a knowledge of what you can do is no answer to the question of what you ought to do. No one knew more about the details of nuclear power than the scientists working at Chalk River and Los Alamos; but as we saw in the last chapter, this did not enable them to decide with confidence what was the right use of this knowledge. We need to remember the fable of the silly angel, who once met the Devil and began to taunt him with the claim that in an age of evolution, all would eventually be well, and so his (the Devil's) fate was therefore doomed. 'Ah, but I too am evolving' was the crushing reply. Knowledge needs wisdom before it can safely be released to men; and it is in the fear of the Lord that the beginnings of wisdom are to be found.

But it is sometimes claimed that technology is ugly—useful perhaps, but devoid of any artistic or aesthetic merit. How woefully inaccurate this is. I should challenge anyone who said that to come with me to the visitors' stand at London Airport. He would find himself surrounded by aeroplanes, one of the most modern examples of technological prowess. I should ask him, as he watched the slow descent of one of these great machines, whether in its steady bird-like quality, or in the elegant shape of its fuselage, he was not watching something whose beauty is to be compared with that of a Greek vase. I am not trying to set up one field of aesthetic satisfaction against another; but I am asserting that there is not a grain of reason why the products of technology should not be beautiful. They often are—as for example, many household kitchen appliances such as mixers and electric irons and washing-machines.

If they are not beautiful, the fault lies as much in ourselves for not insisting that God's gifts may be expressed in beauty just as easily as in ugliness. It was natural for the late Bishop Barnes to speak of a scientific education as 'a purifying influence' and a 'true humanism'. It should be natural for us to agree with George Sarton, the historian of science:

It is true that most men of letters, and, I am sorry to add, not a few scientists, know science only by its material achievements, but ignore its spirit, and see neither its internal beauty nor the beauty it extracts from the bosom of nature . . . a true humanist must know the life of science as he knows the life of art and the life of religion.

Perhaps if we could get that far it would not be long before we found ourselves in substantial agreement with Field-Marshal Smuts, in his Presidential Address to the 1931 Centenary Meeting of the British Association:

Amongst the human values, science ranks with art and with religion. It is a selfless pursuit of truth, and in its vision of order and beauty it partakes of the quality of truth. More and more it is beginning to make a profound aesthetic and religious appeal to thinking people. Indeed it may fairly be said that science is perhaps the clearest revelation of God to our age.

I'm not sure that I go the whole way with this last sentence, but there is one more thing that I must say before I leave this paragraph. It is sometimes supposed that science and technology are graceless, because they never make or admit mistakes. This is utterly false; it is probably more true to say that they alone among the spiritual and intellectual influences of today, are given to admitting error. The scientist is trained to admit his mistakes: he continually seeks them out in his own and other people's work. There is a humility to be found in all the great scientists (though perhaps rather less often among the technologists and the poorer quality scientists) which seems to me to bear a close relation to one of the most characteristic Christian virtues.

I have been speaking of the suspicion with which Christians not infrequently eye the scientist and technologist; and of the ignorance which they often show in regard to their true natures. I must now turn to the grievous misunderstanding of our own Christian doctrine of creation which hinders us from a true appreciation of them. According to our Bible, God is creator not only of man, but of all other things. The book of Genesis starts with a long list of what God made, beginning with the heavens and the earth, passing through the trees, the plants, the animals, and only at the end coming to man. For many years I used to wonder why the writer thought it wise to spend time on such a catalogue. Would it not have been easier to say: 'In the beginning God made all things: then finally He made Adam.' But now I see the reason, and how it was that although man came upon the scene only on the sixth day, at the end of each of the first five days, God had looked at His work and behold, it was good. It was to show that God is concerned with the things of earth, the material things. It was to show us that we must not despise material things, since God made them and enjoyed them: and since they could be the vehicle of His spirit. I do not believe that anyone who really believes this can ever hate technology and machines, just because they are machines. Yet this is precisely what we do; we hate the machine, not so much because in a fit of Luddite enthusiasm we think it will do us out of our job, but because in some way we think it will degrade us. 'I hate and fear science,' wrote George Gissing in his *Ryecroft Papers*, 'because of my conviction that, for a long time to come, if not for ever, it will be the remorseless enemy of mankind. I see it destroying all simplicity and gentleness of life, all the beauty of the world; I see it darkening men's minds and hardening their hearts.' And Otto van der Sprenkel has said the same in a paraphrase of Lord Acton: 'Vacuum cleaners corrupt, washing-machines corrupt absolutely.'

This feeling is not new. In the olden days of Lao-tze in China, the philosopher tells the story of Tzu-kung, a disciple of Confucius, who in the course of his travels came across a simple villager irrigating his vegetable plots. He let himself down into a well, emerged with a pitcher full of water, which he then poured into a suitable channel. It was slow, and not very efficient. So Tzu-kung told him how, by the use of a wooden instrument, he could scoop up water, and save much time and effort. A look of indignation crossed the old man's face, and he laughed scornfully. 'My teacher used to tell me that where there are cunning contrivances there will be cunning behaviour, and where there is cunning be-haviour there will be a cunning heart. . . . It's not that I don't know about this invention, but that I should be ashamed to use it.'

This is a quaint story. But the dangers to which it draws attention are just as grave today. A machine *can* devalue human life. The Bishop of Carlisle tells of a factory which he visited. On one of the huge con-trivances in this factory there was pinned a large notice: 'Do not waste the time of this machine.' This is not without its point, as the following example will show.

Mr Lewis T. Wright, the Chairman of the T.U.C. Scientific Advisory Committee has described a small textile factory with ninety-six latest-type looms, each costing £3,500, and worked by twelve weavers. The overheads on capital investment here amount to £325 a day. For a single weaver to be absent for a day costs the firm nearly £50. In a small concern of this kind, problems of personal relations should be solved fairly easily. But it is easy to see how the machine may come to dominate. Further, this danger will inevitably tend to increase. Thus Norbert Wiener, one of the world experts on automation and machine control, has pointed out that machines will do more and more that men have previously done. So the new industrial revolution is simply bound to devalue the human brain at least in its simple and more routine decisions, just as 'the first industrial revolution, that of the "dark Satanic mills", led to the devaluation of the human arm by the competition of machinery'. I have been in a factory where a dangerous chemical process was carried on. Some of the nitrates involved were exceedingly explosive, so that it was necessary to control the temperature and pressure as accurately as possible, and ensure that safety devices were incorporated wherever they could be. The whole process was controlled automatically, since this was actually safer than if a human being, liable to error, was in charge. I saw large dials indicating how everything was going at every stage of the operation. But in the whole building there was only one man, an engineer sitting at the automatic controls. I wondered what he could do, and so I asked him what action he would take if things began to go wrong. 'I haven't a clue', was his reply. Here, evidently, the machine was more effective

than man. And the same is true in many other direc-
tions. Nearly all computation is now done on machines,
the numerical results are printed automatically because
a good machine will make perhaps one error in twelve
million, but a good human being one in only five thous-
and. Some of the big motor companies are far advanced
in plans to dispense with all workers on their car assembly
lines. The individual items will be brought up by
electronic control at the right time and to the right place.
The screws will be inserted mechanically and tightened
by an electronically guided screwdriver. Agriculture too
shows the same development. Increasingly the dull
ordinary humdrum things that farm labourers used to
do, from milking the cows to sowing the corn, are done
by a machine. In Canada recently I met a man who,
single-handed, farms a huge area. He has every conceivable machine to help him, and in about six months
achieves results, which, in pre-machine days, would
have needed perhaps a dozen labourers in addition to
himself. In the United States we have seen the virtual
disappearance of the unskilled labourer: it is far more
important to have a driver's licence than to possess good
muscles.

But why should the Christian be upset at this change?
Inevitably it raises some problems because every community should care not only for its aged and infirm, but
for those who cannot find adequate work. I would
prefer to regard this new development as a liberating
one. There is no merit in work for work's sake. It is true,
of course, that if the machine takes away from some
people the opportunity of doing those limited things that
nature seems to have made them capable of doing, then
the community should see, in its education for leisure

and enjoyment, that other facilities are made available. There is a call to do some creative thinking here, and not to blame the machine. I shall not deplore the disappearance in Britain of the unskilled labourer, provided only that the climate of our educational system is such that we have taught him a right relationship to the material world and to the world of nature. Neither of these is dependent upon his possession of a high I.Q. Both of them seem to me to follow from the real Christian doctrine of creation.

And for many, the machine has something to give us. I have already referred to the beauty of a modern aeroplane. But sometimes I recall the enthusiasm of a young apprentice for his lathe. He has just learnt to use it, and can machine a piece of metal with an accuracy of one ten-thousandth of an inch. He is thrilled and excited. What shall I say of this? Surely, that it is part of a deeper fulfilment which science and technology make possible. If it is allowed to say so with reverence, I think God enjoys that great precision, and the skill that goes into it. 'Whether it be the erection of a lighthouse on the lonely rock at sea,' said Sir Frederick Bramwell, President of the British Association in 1884, 'whether it be the crossing of rivers, or seas, . . . whether it be in the production of the mighty ocean steamer, or in the spanning of valleys, the piercing of mountains . . . whether it be the encircling of the world with telegraphs—the work of the civil engineer is not of the earth earthy.' But it is only within the framework of a belief in God that this fineness of understanding will be evoked.

There is something else that the machine has to give us. For, as Gilbert Murray once said in a broadcast, 'The machine is a great moral educator. If a horse or a donkey won't go, men lose their tempers and beat it; if a machine won't go, there's no use beating it. You have to think and try till you find what is wrong.' I should not agree with Gilbert Murray if he meant to imply that losing your temper with a horse would help. But I do most certainly agree with him that in its insistence on the significance, the power, the coherence and reliability of thought, the machine is a constant reminder to us that the universe is rational, and in its rationality it tells us something of God. We may not all feel disposed to repeat the words of the astronomer Kepler as he began to understand the motion of the planets, 'I am thinking God's thoughts after Him'; but we can all agree that in an age where unreason and irrationality continually rear their ugly heads, and where whole countries fall victim to an unthinking hatred of 'the Jews', or the 'native peoples', or 'the imperialist war-mongers', or any of the other phobias that rage rampant in different parts of the world, it is of the highest importance that in science, technology, and machines, we have this continual silent reminder that God is Lord of the mind, and that our worship of Him may be not only with our heart and soul and strength, but also with our mind.

But there are dangers. And the Christian has his duty to point to them. If you start to worship God with your mind, but forget the other three parts of the quartet, it will become terribly easy to elevate yourself and, in effect, deny God. The devil is a very intellectual personage! So, when a German newspaper prints an article with the title 'The Machine is our Saviour', or when Mr Nehru, on the occasion of the opening of the world's largest dam recently completed in India, spoke of his pleasure at coming to such a place, because 'these are the temples where I worship', I believe that I can hear a low satanic chuckle. Too great a concentration on the machine can wean us from the fundamentals which the machine should help us to express. This is the greatest temptation of materialism for the average practical Englishman. As Mr Kitson Clark has put it in his book, *The English Heritage*:

The practical business of the world takes up so much time; the problems presented by the good which might be procured, or the evil which must be prevented, become so absorbing that direct interest in what is spiritual begins to fade. In due course the importance of spiritual issues seems to be solely derived from their probable effect on the material world; people are to be virtuous that they may better serve the needs of your policy, not because virtue has any inherent value in itself.

This is probably the gravest danger in all our considerations of technology and the machine—that we get so busy with it that we forget the spiritual background without which all our expertise will become positively harmful. No one has put this better than the Duke of Edinburgh, when in 1956 he called his Study Conference at Oxford. For the first time in history there came together members of the Commonwealth and Empire concerned with a single problem—the impact of industrialization upon the varied communities that were represented, and the devising of plans to mitigate its evils and encourage its good features. For three weeks managers, technicians, trade unionists, and others met to discuss and study the human problems which they were having to face in their day-to-day work. But before they started these discussions His Royal Highness spoke to them:

Because the world we live in is so largely subject to science, engineering and industrial production, and because industrialized countries are generally more prosperous and seem to enjoy a higher standard of living, it is very easy to get into the habit of thinking of industry as an end in itself. It is, of course, only a means to an end. The community in fact is more important than the industry. It may not be very easy to decide quite what we are aiming at in this modern world of ours, but whatever the target we must take into account that all people are primarily citizens and not just workers with a bit of private life. I see no advantage in a prosperous and powerful state if it is to be achieved at the expense of human freedom and happiness. . . . The criterion is the happiness, satisfaction, contentment or whatever word you care to choose, of the individual as citizen and not merely as a worker, and of communities present and future who depend for their livelihood upon industry.

I met those words first, not in the subsequent full report of the Duke's speech, but in a small book giving one man's reflections on the whole Study Conference, and bearing the very apt title, *The Challenge of Change*. There can be no doubt about the challenge: if it is to be met, it will not be because Christians have shied away from the social implications of a machine age, but because they have made the only really important contribution which no one but they can make—which is that 'the happiness, satisfaction, contentment' of any individual are bound up with the fact that he, like all other individuals, is a child of God, with the freedom, the privileges and the responsibilities that attach to this family inheritance. The Christian community, though it may have very little technical knowledge of these things, enjoys the responsible task of setting the atmosphere and background of thought out of which the 'challenge of change' will be faced. As a Trade Union leader recently put it: 'We have discovered . . . that the social implications of rapidly increasing productivity . . . can become the bottleneck of production, and that unless these social problems are solved in parallel with our technical problems, progress will be seriously retarded.' Who better than the Christian has the right and duty to proclaim that the machine is for man, not man for the machine? If we can persuade our world of this, then most of the evils that men dread about the influence of technology, will die a sterile death.

Sometimes I think that the Christian community grievously underestimates the difficulties that face it as it speaks this message. These difficulties exist at every level of our society. Thus, when any government says that from three per cent to five per cent unemployment is 'good' for industry, we have to remind them that their use of the word 'good' is not a fully Christian one. When, in the interests of rationalization, factories are closed in one part of the country, and concentrated in another, we have to assert that there are moral obligations on management which it has no right to neglect. Similarly when (as happened to me not very long ago) I ask one of the major Trade Union leaders what contribution his Union is making to new thought about his industry, and he replies 'That's not our concern, that belongs to management'; or when another Trade Union leader says, 'The trades unions have never been opposed to change. Indeed, they exist to create change—change in the form of higher wages, shorter hours, more holidays', I feel that I want to shout to them that this is one of the most selfish ways of expressing the world-wide solidarity of men. And when I learn that men have been on strike for months because they cannot settle who should hammer a rivet into wood or metal, I begin to see that my apparently harmless statement about the 'freedom, privileges, and responsibilities' of the family of God will become like high explosive if it is taken literally. If there is any moral to be drawn from all this, it is that there is a clear Christian vocation into industry—not primarily as factory chaplains or padres, where the status is not well-defined, and where it is almost impossible to be effective beyond the level of dealing with personal and domestic difficulties. This is admittedly very important. But there is an even more important need for Christians to enter industry as workers and managers; and, as they do their work, continually to ponder on the rightness and the wrongness of it. The workings of the Holy Spirit are not confined to Church meetings; they may be found in the hesitant, puzzled, uncertain, tentative efforts of Christians at their union meeting or in industrial consultation. If our industrial life is to be made more wholesome, the Church must speak. But much of what it says will have to be said from inside and not from outside; and most of us will have a lot to learn before we shall have very much to say.

To a large extent the personal issues which I have just been describing are closely related to the loss of tradition which I described in Chapter 1, and which seemed to be fundamental to the malaise of our generation. For in olden times a man knew his boss, and there were well-established traditional attitudes which resulted from this. The only exceptions—and not always even then—were the slave communities, where the question of rights did not arise. But today the pattern of industry

changes so fast that the traditional attitudes are mean-
ingless. It means nothing to a railway porter that the
nation is now his employer, and very few industrial
workers have any idea how large is the financial stake
which their various unions hold in industry. But if the
word 'employer' cannot be personalized, it is difficult to
expect loyalty, and it is not long before 'most workers
work on the basis that management is guilty until it is
proved innocent'. This is not the place to elaborate
some of the devices which are being tried (e.g. the
Hawthorne experiment where a bunch of girls worked
marvellously well once they knew precisely how their
work fitted into the total pattern of the factory): but it
is important that Christians should think of these things.
In the last resort these experiments work well not because
they are clever experiments—though of course they may
be very clever—but because they succeed in translating
into the language of an industrial scheme the Christian
vocabulary about the freedom and responsibilities of the
children of God.

So far this chapter has been concerned with the
problems and the difficulties associated with the rise of
the second industrial revolution. But it would be wrong
to conclude this broad survey of its relation to the
Christian faith without examining one way in which the
greater freedom of today makes possible a fuller life.
Let us begin by asking why it is a good thing to raise the
standard of living, or to increase the amount of leisure.
It certainly does not follow that a man will necessarily be
happier if he has a motor car instead of a bicycle, or a
fortnight's holiday-with-pay instead of just the August
Bank Holiday week-end. The biographies of an earlier
generation show that people could be happy without any

of these 'luxuries'. Any attempt to tie the coming of the Kingdom of God to a forty-hour week, or a guaranteed wage, is the result of a serious confusion about the nature of this Kingdom. It is better to start, not with ourselves, but with the under-developed countries of the world; for there the situation is more clearly seen. 'Throughout most of history', says a writer on adult education, who is concerned about the use of leisure,

work, for a majority, has been exhausting, enfeebling, or even degrading. For a minority it has been an exhilarating experience in the exercise of acquired skills, or it has been aesthetically or socially satisfying. It is now possible to conceive of work, in technically advanced countries, as offering the second alternative to far more people.

How much more true this must be in technically non-advanced countries! I am not claiming that work, even hard physical work, is necessarily bad. For it can be accepted with grace and it can become a sacrament. But I am saying that the wider a man's choice to do this or that or something else, the richer does his character become, at least potentially. It is no answer to say that if we reduce his weekly working hours from forty-five to forty, he will merely spend the hours which are saved at the dogs or in the pub. We diminish 'that part of life in which a man is driven by necessity, and increase that in which he chooses for himself, the noble or the ignoble, the ugly or the beautiful, the true or the false, and in choosing learns by experience where the difference lies'. Even if people do not seize these opportunities, and the result is that they choose the lower rather than the higher; even if not many people are yet capable of making the most of their new opportunities—it is not

for us to judge. When we pause to think of the freedom
that God has given us, and the errors of judgement that
we have made as we used or misused it, we shall see that
all our Christian insight is for taking risks. Here again
the Christian has his responsibility of leadership. For
unless there are people who know these things and
proclaim them in their lives, there is a smaller chance
that others will make the right choice. Science and
technology are good, but they are not enough. 'I saw the
science I worshipped and the aircraft I loved', said
Charles Lindbergh in *The Spirit of St Louis*, 'destroying
the civilization I expected them to serve, and which I
thought as permanent as Earth itself. Now I under
stand that spiritual truth is more essential to a nation
than the mortar in its cities' walls.' It comes to this
that the standards by which men make their choice out
of the greater freedom which is now theirs, must be set
by people with that sort of insight into human nature
which the Christian gospel provides. 'One determinant
of a nation's greatness', writes Dr Detlev Bronk in his
chairman's foreword to the eighth annual report of the
U.S. National Science Foundation, 'is its courage to
choose between the important and the less important.
A nation achieves greatness by determined devotion to
the things that matter most as it sacrifices the un
essential.'

I am writing these paragraphs shortly after one of the
most glaring examples of the Christian community's
failure to provide such standards for ordinary people. A
few months ago a General Election was fought in
Britain; and the issue that loomed largest was symbolized
by the slogan of one party, 'You've never had it so
good', and by the other party, 'If you vote for us

you'll have it better'. Now the raising of the standard of living in this country is something of which I approve, and would gladly work for. But I felt ashamed for my Christian convictions, that we did not see that this choice between the important and the less important was one where we should have been far more vocal than most of us were. In the nineteenth century the 'Free-Church conscience' had political repercussions. In the twentieth century the Christian conscience should have insisted that instead of this lesser issue, our candidates dealt more with the greater ones. Why was it that questions of peace, population, and world food (some of which we shall consider in the next chapter) were almost totally disregarded? This is not the way to the greatness of which Dr Bronk speaks.

There is another aspect of man's larger freedom which is relevant here. It concerns the greater responsibility which the machine age has given to a greater number of people. When I take possession of my new motor car, I have to depend upon its brakes: when I fly in an aeroplane, I have to rely upon the efficiency and reliability of hundreds of people, from the men who riveted the bodywork to the petrol-men who filled the tanks with the right liquid and to the right level. I accept all these things on trust, but I ought occasionally to remind myself that greater care is something new in most people's lives. It was not a matter of life or death whether the corn was evenly sowed at exactly the optimum moment. But it *is* a matter of life or death that the electric signals on the railway work correctly. In a thousand ways the work that men do has become more dangerous, in the sense that their mistakes carry responsibility for larger disasters. We may not like it, we may be frightened of it; but we cannot escape it. For my own part I believe this wider sharing of responsibility is good, for it serves to exalt the dignity of daily work, and expresses our mutual dependence. Christian people, who have their reasons for believing in both of these, ought therefore to be glad that modern technology offers this growth in personal responsibility. The fact that there are still train accidents because someone fails at the personal level, or that sometimes an aeroplane crashes for mistakes that could have been avoided, is no ultimate argument for any kind of return to the past.

And so we come to the end of this chapter. I have tried to show that many of the fears which Christian people exhibit towards technology are really without a solid basis. We do not need to be suspicious of it as if it must inevitably wean us away from the faith; we do not need to imagine that it has now made God unnecessary, nor that it is without any excellence of its own; we do not need to think of the machine as our implacable enemy. For if we understand our Christian doctrine of creation, the material things of earth may become the vessels in which we handle the things of heaven: and the greater freedom which we now enjoy—freedom to choose, freedom from oppressive physical labour, freedom to accept or deny the responsibilities that arise in all industrial production—may become one of the ways by which we fulfil God's destiny for us, and glorify Him in our daily work. Of course there are risks. But if it were not so, there would be no reward for reaching out. Our God is a refining fire.

CHAPTER FOUR

Relation to the Christian Faith—Some Particular Examples

IN THE LAST chapter we were concerned with some very general comments which a Christian may be expected to make, when he considers modern technology. These comments were necessarily in the form of broad principles. It is instructive, however, to turn from the general to the particular, and to see how these principles work out in practice. In this chapter, therefore, we shall choose some definite situations, of considerable topical significance, and look at them in more detail. These situations will illustrate the application of the general principles of our last chapter, and at the same time will show the close intertwining of the good and the bad which seems to characterize our modern world. They will also show that unless we prepare ourselves for big changes in the future, we shall eventually find ourselves in an explosive situation. The time is not yet 'five minutes to midnight'; but in some respects it is not far off. First let us deal with the world's supply of power; then with the related problems of food and population. This will lead to a discussion of the changes which science and technology are causing in family life, and finally to a consideration of some implications of all this in our educational system.

A—POWER

It has been said that the scale on which any community can make use of energy is the simplest criterion of its development. For power is closely correlated with industrial development, with productivity, and with living standards. Power, i.e. energy, may be called the wheels of civilization.

We can see this very easily if we think of the many ways in which our lives depend on our ability to control power for our own use. I wake up in the morning, and switch on the electric light—power; I go to the bathroom and wash in hot water provided by an immersion heater —power again; I eat my breakfast cooked on a gas-cooker in a room warmed by a coal fire; I go to work on a bicycle into the back wheel of which I have inserted a tiny petrol motor—huge steel works have made the frame of this bicycle, and a hundred different industries have been required in order that the oil from the Middle East should be brought up from the wells, transported in tankers and finally refined to produce petrol. Other heavy industries are needed that there should be fertilizers for the crops that give me my breakfast. All of this depends in an ultimate sense on the possession of power.

There are several things that must be said about this. In the first place, power is being used at a tremendously accelerating rate; in the second place, its use is exceedingly uneven in different parts of the world; and thirdly, unless we can do something big for the underdeveloped parts of the world, they will never have any chance of reaching the same standard of life as we have in the West. These three points deserve elaboration.

It is not always recognized how rapidly we are

increasing our world use of power. Suppose that we introduce a suitable unit in which it is convenient to measure the world's power supplies. The quantity Q has been suggested, where $1Q =$ a million million million British Thermal Units. $1Q$ is about 150 times the British annual supply of coal. It has been estimated that in the first eighteen centuries of the Christian era the total world consumption of power was about $9Q$, which is the equivalent of $\frac{1}{2}Q$ per century. In 1850 this had grown to $1Q$ per century: in 1950, however, the rate was $10Q$ per century, so that the world is now using power at a rate ten times as fast as one hundred years ago. Estimates suggest that by the end of the present century we are likely to increase this figure by a factor of another twenty, leading to a rate of no less than $2Q$ per year. Such a rate of increase is almost staggering. Thus over half of the total amount of coal used in the world's history has been burnt in the last twenty-five years, and half of the oil in the last twelve years. But this presents some serious problems. For the world's resources are by no means unlimited. The coal reserves of Britain, for example, are estimated to be sufficient for about 250 years at our present rate of mining, though the difficulties of winning this coal will increase as the best seams become exhausted. The best coking coals (from West Durham) will last only for about fifty years. This situation was brought home to me very vividly a few years ago, when I went down one of the Somersetshire coal mines. When we got to the actual face, I saw that the seam was a bare ten inches thick. How much more difficult this is than in the older, now nearly exhausted seams in Yorkshire where the depth was often ten feet! Peat will not materially help, being equivalent to only about one tenth of the coal reserves; oil, wind, and water power are inadequate. Most of our coal was laid down in the carboniferous era about two hundred and fifty million years ago. It is quite irreplaceable, and we are burning it so fast that in the second industrial revolution we shall soon find ourselves with relatively little left to burn.

We may conclude from this that Professor Bhabha was right when he claimed that atomic power was the only foreseeable source of energy for the future. World supplies of uranium and thorium amount to energy of the order of 1,700 Q, so that there will be plenty of atomic energy of the kind that we now extract in our nuclear power stations to last until we have learnt the last great secret in this field—which is the control of hydrogen fusion. Well might Dr Bhabha add: 'For the full industrialization of the under-developed countries, for the continuance of our civilization and its further development, atomic energy is not merely an aid; it is an absolute necessity.' And another writer has put it in much the same way: 'The outlook on the fossil situation . . . is dark. . . . Even if present estimates of reserves turn out to be wide of the mark, the time-table of fossil fuel production will be extended only a few years. The technical decades ahead are sure to be tumultuous.'

We have just seen how rapidly our use of power is expanding. Now let us see how uneven it is. At the present time 82 per cent of the useful energy is consumed by 33 per cent of the world's population. The table below shows the rate of consumption of power per year in different countries. This rate is expressed in terms of tons of coal per person per year, but of course it will be realized that all the various sources of power are included, such as coal, oil, water and wind.

U.S.A.	10 tons per head per year
U.K.	7 ,, ,, ,,
Italy	1 ,, ,, ,,
India	10 cwt ,, ,,
Egypt	9 cwt ,, ,,

This unevenness of power is paralleled by similar inequalities in the world's income. Thus in the nineteen richest countries of the world 16 per cent of the world's population enjoy 66 per cent of the world's income, whereas in the fifteen poorest countries, 50 per cent of the world's population has only 9 per cent of the world's income. One person in three of the working population of the world receives less than £18 per year; no less than two out of three receive less than £70 a year. In India and China the weekly income is less than the equivalent of eleven shillings in English money. Evidently standards of living run closely related to power.

What this means may be appreciated if we compare the situation today with what it was 200 years ago. It has been estimated that the present-day American citizen has available 2,500 times as much power as his ancestor two centuries earlier. This makes him the possessor of the equivalent of sixty slaves! The position in Britain is very similar: and it shows how profoundly our times differ from those of our predecessors. Similar differences exist between countries. Thus industrialized Denmark with a population of four and a half millions can produce more than China with four hundred millions.

This discussion of the inequalities of the world's power supply leads inevitably to our third point: which is that the developed and industrialized part of the world is now called to a great creative task—of sharing its wealth.

This is not easy, however charitably minded we may be. We can see this if we ask how it is that, after lying almost stationary for about 2,000 years, our standard of living rose in the first industrial revolution to be more than ten times that in the non-developed countries. In his Presidential Address to the British Association in 1957 Professor Blackett referred to this as a 'take-off into sustained growth'. In his own words:

In a typical pre-industrial country, three-quarters or more of the population may be engaged in agriculture, and wealth tends to remain constant or rises but slowly. Savings and gross investment are low, some 5 per cent or less of the national income, that is, only about enough to maintain a static economy by paying for the depreciation of existing wealth. After 'take-off', savings and gross investment rise until some 15 per cent of the national income is available for gross investment, leaving around 10 per cent for net new productive investment. On the average in the West today such new investment results in a rise of total income of about 3 per cent a year. Allowing for the population rise of some 1 per cent, this gives an increase of wealth per head around 2 per cent a year. The fraction of the population engaged in agriculture steadily falls as social development and industrialization proceed, and agriculture itself becomes partly industrialized and so much more efficient.'

Now as things are at the present moment, the Western world is saving and investing some £30 per head per year, in plant and machinery to create more wealth. This may be compared with the pre-industrial countries of Asia where there is a grand total of only about £20 per head per year to live on. The West is therefore saving more per head than the East is spending on everything. It is not surprising therefore that the gap between the two civilizations is actually widening. It is often claimed that our standard of living is increasing at least twice as fast as that in India.

One reason for this is indubitably finance (though in a later chapter we shall say something about a more human factor). It requires a capital of £5,000-10,000 for every man engaged in heavy industry, and about a third of this for medium and light industry. If we really believe that we are members of one family, then we ought surely to be deeply dissatisfied that so little is done to help. An immediate need is for about £1,000 million a year, which is only about £1 for each of the thousand million inhabitants involved. This is equivalent to one per cent of the West's income. Britain's share of £150 million per year would delay by less than one year the expected rise of fifty per cent in our standard of living in the next twenty-five years. I would like to quote again from Professor Blackett:

Scientists and technologists have a special responsibility in this matter, since it is their genius and their skill which alone can bring the material basis of happiness within the reach of all. The progress of the natural sciences, the West's greatest achievement, has been based on experiment. Let us now make the great social experiment to spread the benefits of our labours. At present they reach only a few. A 'have-not' country, bound like a modern Tantalus by the chains of its lack of capital, gazes with unquenchable thirst on the growing riches of modern technology which it cannot enjoy.

Here, in this 'social experiment', the Christian has his role. It is not the role of the scientist and the economist working out these various ratios. But it is the responsibility of seeing the need, recognizing our national share of it, and setting the pattern of thought which will make it possible for the scientist and the politician to do their part in the biggest joint enterprise that this world has ever seen.

B—FOOD AND POPULATION

The problem of power is in a certain sense an impersonal one. But the problems of food and population most certainly are not. For we must all eat if we are to live, and it is a matter of the most immediate significance to us if the population grows at such a rate that there is not enough food to go round. As we shall see in a moment, our world is on the point of reaching this situation.

Let us consider the population problem first. There are really three phases in the growth of the human race. In the far-off days of pre-agriculture, when men lived by eating berries from the trees and occasional raw meat from animals that they had trapped, the population had to be small. There was simply not enough to eat to support any larger numbers. But about 7,000 years ago agriculture developed, with regular planting of seeds and harvesting of crops. As a result more than 500 people could be supported in areas where previously only one person had been able to survive. At the beginning of the Christian era the world population was around two hundred million (about four times the present population of Britain). There seems to have been only a very gradual increase until the middle of the seventeenth century, after which the increase became extremely rapid. By A.D. 1900 it was fifteen hundred million; between 1650 and 1920 it doubled itself twice over, though the first doubling took 200 years, and the second only about seventy years. It now seems to be increasing in such a way that its next doubling will take only sixty years. This is at the rate of one and one third per cent per annum. We are adding nearly 100,000 new people every day; and even this rate is increasing. By the end of this century the world population may conceivably reach as many as seven thousand million people.

Such an expansion, which a recent writer has called 'The Population Explosion' will inevitably cause food problems. For the largest numerical increase (though not necessarily the largest proportional increase) comes from precisely those parts of the world where the standard of living is lowest, and the food supply already inadequate. It is worth reminding ourselves that of every five human beings two are perpetually hungry, two others are intermittently hungry (according to the behaviour of the monsoons or the floods), and only one is satisfied as we are. This pitiful situation is found in the backward parts of Europe and, even worse, in the countries of the East. It was Gandhi who said: 'To the millions who have to go without two meals a day the only acceptable form in which God dare appear is food.' And it was a young boy in the Eastern Zone of Germany who, when asked if he knew about Jesus Christ, replied: 'No; is he still alive? And will he bring us food to eat?'

We may reasonably ask whether such a degree of hunger is inevitable. Thomas Malthus, writing of these things in 1798, asserted that population would necessarily grow in number until all the available food was used up, and then, by famine or by war, or by some other means, there would be maintained just as large a population as the world's resources would permit. Indeed, Colin Clark has pointed out that in the same year that Malthus was writing his famous essay, Jenner was publishing his proposals for vaccination against smallpox—which probably did more than any single factor to bring about the nineteenth-century increase in population; for up to that time smallpox used to kill one person in every thousand each year in Britain. But Malthus stated that Jenner's work was all a waste of time because 'principles of population' indicated that, even if he were successful, some other disease would grow up to take the place of smallpox and keep the population steady. Today, one hundred and sixty years afterwards, we see that Malthus was wrong: the population of Britain increased greatly, but without additional hunger. We are now better fed than at any time since human beings first inhabited this land.

If the world is to avoid being hungry, it must be because it produces sufficient food per person. And this will require space to cultivate. However skilful a community may be, it cannot grow enough food if the population is so large that there is no room left for agriculture. In the simpler forms of agriculture, using hand tools, a man can economically occupy about five acres, and approximately feed seven people. But sometimes there is not this much space available. In Japan, for example, although there is the highest yield of rice anywhere in Asia, there is only one seventh of an acre of cultivable land per head. There is no wonder that the daily calorie intake, of about 2,000 calories per head, is inadequate. And the larger the population grows, the more essential will it be for Japan to import food. It is clear that this food will have to be grown in some of the less productive parts of the world. Enormous developments are absolutely essential if we would avoid the population-food-explosion. Thus in Persia there are over 400 million acres of ground that are potentially cultivable, yet only three per cent of them are cultivated. Here, in the last resort, it is an inadequate and unchristian view of man which is partly responsible. 'Tradition says that life in the country is composed of five things—earth, water, seeds, animals, and work. The first four belong to the land-owner—we have a right to a fifth.' In such a situation the interpretative role of the Christian is clear enough. But this is not the only need. If we would feed our world properly, by the year A.D. 2000 we shall need fifty million tons of nitrogenous fertilizers every year, where now we have only six million tons. This alone is a tremendous undertaking, requiring large-scale planning on a scale which is bigger than a purely national one. It is only too true that the problem of world food is a world problem. It is a technical problem—in the provision of tractors and artificial fertilizers; it is a biological problem—for a knowledge of photosynthesis (why 'grass is green') could radically change the situation of mankind; it is a political problem —for these immense activities have to be co-ordinated on national and international levels; and it is a religious problem—since without an impulse to do these things and make these plans, no progress will be achieved.

It is fortunate for us that the best estimates suggest that, if we really were prepared to go ahead, using our land to the best advantages, the world could support a population several times larger than at present. Colin Clark has given reasons for saying that our earth could sustain a population of thirty thousand million people, i.e. about ten times the present total. Even if this figure is exaggerated, the fact of abject poverty is a constant disgrace to us. The Christian community should continue to insist that our country should think globally about these things. The financing of the necessary projects will be such that only world organizations like the World Health Organization (W.H.O.) and the Food and Agriculture Organization (F.A.O.) are ultimately able to cope with it.

There is one final aspect of the population problem on which Christian opinion is gravely divided, but where some kind of action seems to be inevitable. This is not the place to argue the rights and wrongs of contraception. But without some techniques which simple people can understand and practise, there seems little hope that the population growth will significantly diminish in the near future. An ordinary healthy woman can expect to have a child every two and a half years of married life. An average fertility of six or seven is now found among many of the under-developed countries of Asia. The more effective our medicines become in reducing deaths of new-born babies, the more catastrophic will the increase in population become. In India already in the last thirty years the expectation of life has risen from 20 to 32. Julian Huxley has described an inquiry recently conducted by the Indian Health Ministry. In one village about three quarters of the married women said they would like to learn some method for limiting their families. For myself, I cannot help feeling that we ought to help them, and I am persuaded that the recently developed oral contraceptive may become one of the greatest benefits that the medical science and technology of the West have to offer to the overcrowded East. It is certainly time that the West acknowledged, in unsentimental terms, its responsibility in the matter of population, and cleared away the present muddle in its mind.

C—FAMILY LIFE

It is not always recognized how significant science and technology have been in the past in influencing the pattern of family life. There are two aspects of this influence which we must discuss. But since both of them stretch out far beyond the bounds within which our discussion can be allowed to stretch here, it will be necessary to concentrate on certain major issues only. The aspects to be dealt with are, first the changing age of life, and the effect that this has on the shape of a normal family; and second the increased standard of living in the home itself, with its consequential influence on the significance of the home as a centre of activity.

In 1951 we took our last decennial census of the population. The Registrar-General published the statistical results of this census as a basis on which the Government Actuary, and others, could prepare effective life tables for insurance purposes. In these tables it was shown that the expectation of life at birth for a girl was a little over $71\frac{1}{2}$ years, and for a boy about $66\frac{1}{2}$ years. The difference between these figures is unimportant for our present purposes, being due to the fact that certain hereditary diseases are sex-linked: that is, they are normally transmitted only in the sex-chromosome responsible for the child being a boy and not a girl. The average of these two figures is 69 years. When the next census comes to be taken, in 1961, it is almost certain that the corresponding average will be distinctly over 70, and it may be as high as 72.

There is a very great difference here from the days of

FSTC

the Old Testament, where three score years and ten represented the total life span. For now more than half our population may expect to live beyond this traditional figure. But the difference is much greater than would be expected. There are, unhappily, very few reliable estimates of the average age of life in earlier times. The best figures for the eighteenth century are Swedish. A table based on birth, death and total population between 1755 and 1776 shows an expectation of life of 33 for boys and 36 for girls. It is likely that much the same was true in Wesley's England. In the big towns the condition was worse: the inhabitants who lived around Wesley's Chapel in City Road had an expectation of life of only 19 years (in Stockholm at that time it was about 16!). Some particularly tough people—or, maybe, lucky people—lived to a ripe old age. John Wesley himself lived to be only a little less than 90. But these were the exceptions to the much younger averages.

During the years since then the change from an average of 35 to an average of 70 has taken place. It is largely the combined result of better scientific knowledge—of food, vitamins, hormones, general medicine, vaccination, penicillin and the sulfa drugs—and of better technology—in such things as cleaner water supplies and improved sewerage. It is hard for us today to realize the appalling conditions which existed even up to moderately recent times. Medieval streets often had a central gutter, in principle closed by huge stone slabs. All refuse, including faecal matter, was thrown into this trench, and then it was collected and dumped outside the town at irregular intervals. The stench was awful. Graunt, in his *Observations* of 1662 asserts that 'the Fumes, Steams and Stenches of London do so medicate the air about it that it becomes capable of little more'. It is not hard to understand why, only a few years later, the Great Plague could spread so effectively. Almost the only way to escape it was to flee from London and the towns. It was thus that Isaac Newton probably saved his own life, by retreating to his father's farm in the country at Woolsthorpe in Lincolnshire.

The influence of technology was felt as soon as decent water supplies became available. The provision of large amounts of purified water is essentially a technological problem. But when it was provided, the population increased rapidly. In Britain this took place in the nineteenth century, as a necessary corollary of the growing first industrial revolution. The foundation of our modern water-law goes back only to the Waterworks Clauses Acts of 1847 and the Public Health Act of 1848, though there had been partially successful efforts to get water to London and a few other cities for about 250 years previously.

The most striking result of this combination of medical science and technology was a drastic fall in infant mortality. Fewer children died in their first few years of life. A personal illustration may remind us of the way in which this affected family attitudes. My old grannie, when she met her acquaintances in the street, would say to them: 'How many have you reared?' But my wife, when she meets her friends, says to them: 'How many have you got?' In that simple illustration there is represented a world of change. For life, particularly child life, was cheap: now it is precious and dear.

Today, in this second industrial revolution, a further change is taking place. But this time we are increasing

the age at the end of life, and not at the beginning. We
are living longer. The operative causes are still better
science and better medicine, and none of us would wish it
otherwise. But several new problems have thereby been
forced upon us. In the first place we are changing the
balance of the population. In some Scottish villages the
village school has had to be closed because there aren't
enough children to keep it going. And in others I have
come across cases where a child hardly had any other
children of its own age to play with. Certainly we are
discovering more and more that we are tending towards
a predominantly old community. A characteristic
feature of the 1950s has been the establishment of
Homes for the Aged, of all kinds (though the Christian
Community has every reason for feeling some small pride
that its efforts have been so effective). But there is much
more to do. For modern technology is much faster and
more demanding than it used to be. A recent survey
sponsored by the Nuffield Foundation has shown that in
our increasingly mechanized civilization the wear-and-
tear is such that although men live longer, at age sixty
five no less than ten per cent of all male workers are
totally incapacitated. By some means the community
must find some way to ease the burden of the 'ageing
worker'. But it must also provide some satisfying func
tion for them to fulfil. Modern technology may have
made us more secure against the hazards of non-human
nature, but it has left us much more vulnerable to the
hazards of human nature, expressing themselves in
human conflicts and human purposelessness. We shall
have more to say about this in a later paragraph.

The pattern of family life has also been changed by
the rise in standard of living. Many people are familiar

with the two surveys made in York by Seebohm Rown-
tree, in 1899 and 1936. Amongst other findings these
surveys showed that the percentage of the working
population living in the worst poverty had improved
from 15·6 in 1899 to only 6·8 in 1936. In 1960 the figure
would have dropped to almost zero. We know, as an
indication of this drop, that the average standard of
living in Britain has been raised by twenty per cent in
the last ten years, and most of this increase is among the
poorer people. Partly this is the result of taxation:
thus a man earning £10,000 a year would have kept
forty-three per cent of it in 1938, but only twenty-three
per cent in 1948, after income tax had been removed.
Partly also it is a very genuine levelling in income.

This silent revolution shows itself in a variety of ways.
In 1957, for example, the National Food Survey showed
that the average working-class family spent ten shillings
a head weekly on food, and the average middle-class
family only twelve shillings. There is hardly any significant difference. It is the same with other things, the
gadgets with which we decorate our homes and make
them more efficient. During the last ten years the
number of television sets has increased from one in
every hundred homes to two in every three homes. The
number of washing-machines has increased tenfold,
refrigerators trebled, and vacuum cleaners doubled.
Our homes, two million of which are post-war, are
brighter places, we are proud to live in them, and they
attract our care and our time in keeping them up to date
and at least 'equal to the Joneses'.

Several results have followed from this. There is now
no longer any need to escape from our home. So we do
not go to the cinema (weekly attendances have dropped

in this period from twenty-five million to nine million); we do not go to meetings (not even a General Election can draw a crowd); we do not go to church, nor do we meet people and have to adjust ourselves to them, as in less fortunate days. I realized this very sharply a few weeks ago when, after an interval of fifteen years, I visited a Church and Community Centre on a new Housing Estate. The Warden told me that he could no longer gather the people together as we used to do, because 'they would only come to the Community Centre when there was nothing "good" on the "telly".' A recent writer has called this the 'home-centred society'. Not even the increasing ownership of a motor car affects this inward-turning tendency, since most new owners treat their car as a detachable extra room to their house, to be used on weekdays to travel to and from work without the need to use public transport; and at weekends as a small mobile room to be taken to the seaside or the country and in which they can sit in isolation watching what goes on around them.

Some of this is no doubt exaggerated. But what stands out is that until the breakaway of the teenage child, families are now more house- and self-centred. Their interests, and their values, are correspondingly restricted. Less and less do they identify themselves with the social life of the community. The status of women has changed. Since the good husband is now the domesticated husband, the wife becomes the reigning monarch. Nowhere may this be seen more clearly than in the most technologically developed country, i.e. America.

In much of all this the Christian will find satisfaction. The unimaginative response of the first industrial revolution, which led to the squalor of the back-to-back houses of Yorkshire's woollen towns and the insanitary Scottish tenements of Dundee and Glasgow, required to be compensated by the provision of better housing. Much of the past was a standing reproach to us. But that is no excuse for an unimaginative response in our second industrial revolution. It may be true—as I hope it is—that prosperity is a better starting-point than poverty for the growth of a full human being. But it is just as easy to go to the devil in a motor car as on foot. Man is made for co-operation, and he loses in dignity and character when his contacts with his fellow men are diminished. 'Fellowship is Heaven', said William Morris, 'and lack of Fellowship is Hell. And the deeds that ye do on earth, it is for the sake of Fellowship that ye do them.' Surely if this is true, then the Christian community has a responsibility to see that out of the material good of these last years there shall spring spiritual good and not evil. For we understand what Fellowship means, and we know something of the spiritual resources which make the 'I-thou' relation fruitful beyond measure. The life of the family finds its true fulfilment in the life of the community: but this is only possible when we share a common view of man, and so ultimately of God. We must therefore understand the changes that modern technology has brought both to family and community life; and without denying the great improvements of the last fifty years, we must conceive a strategy which will keep open the wider channels of communication now in danger.

D—EDUCATION

This discussion of the family leads naturally to our last concern in this chapter—education. This is not the place to discuss education in general; nor to consider the changes in educational practice in the last fifty years. Rather we must ask whether the coming of the second industrial revolution suggests any particular new issues for education, and their relation to our fundamental beliefs as Christian educators.

But first let us remind ourselves of what education means in the life of our community. Since every child participates in it, it is one of the few activities in which the whole community is involved. Decisions which we make about it affect every child; and they do this at the most impressionable age. In 1960 more than three-quarters of a million children will reach the age of fifteen and leave school. By 1962 this figure will rise to its peak of 929,000. What, if anything, are we expecting them to know about the matters with which this book is concerned?

First of all, they ought to know something about science and technology. There is a good precedent here from which we may learn. The first industrial revolution gathered much of its origin and its impetus in Britain. The native ability and ingenuity of a Watt and a Stephenson, coupled with the ease of access to coal and iron, made this almost inevitable. Britain was undisputed leader by the middle of the nineteenth century. But before long she began to lose her place. The rise of German and American heavy industry, and Continental chemistry, led to our relative decline. A large part of this decline must be ascribed to the failure which we showed in Britain to recognize within our educational system the nature of the developments which science was making possible. The first university laboratory in which undergraduates did experiments in physics was at King's College, London, as late as the 1870's, when Clerk

Maxwell began to suggest that if a student was to learn physics for his degree, he ought to possess some capability to do experiments. Other universities followed, some of them considerably later. It would be a serious error if we repeated this in the second industrial revolution, and, in fact, since this new revolution is more centrally based on science, it is more imperative that our educational system should pay some attention to it. (In parenthesis let it be added that precisely the same applies to the training of men for the Ministry. But there is almost no indication that we are aware of this. In the Report of the Methodist Probationers' Committee for 1958-9 we find that probationers must study three books on the Old Testament, three books on the New Testament, two books on theology and—for the summer!—one of the five topics, Church History, Philosophy, Comparative Religion, Psychology, and Social Studies. There is not even the faintest vestige of reference to either science or technology, whose influences will be the most formative of all in the lives of many of the people to whom these probationers are shortly to minister.) We must pay some attention to these things because it is one of the purposes of education that it should help us to understand ourselves and our environment. The ancient Greek would say: γνῶθι σεαυτόν ('know thyself'). And the Christian will add that out of that fuller knowledge comes richer worship.

It seems to me an inevitable corollary of all this that no child should be allowed to pass through our whole educational system today without some acquaintance with science. In older days the classics were the natural mode of expression among cultured people. It was therefore entirely natural that classics should form part of the backbone of a decent education. It is no disparagement of the classics to say that now that role belongs to science. Some understanding of science, its mode of activity, its discipline, its authority, and its claims is as much a part of general education today as the ability to construe a Latin or Greek text was two hundred years ago. I am not suggesting that the classics have nothing to teach us—the example of America is a clear enough pointer to what happens when we completely neglect them—and I hope that we shall continue to keep the best from our past tradition. I doubt, indeed, whether we can do our science teaching properly unless we see it in relation to its past; and I never tire of pointing out to the ultra-modern schoolboy that the word 'atom' was not the product of this generation's nuclear physicists, but of Democritus, Lucretius, and Leukippus, thousands of years ago.

It is important that we should teach some science, and, no less, some technology. When the Duke of Edinburgh was opening the new extension of the Manchester College of Science and Technology in November 1957, he made this point very clearly:

The important thing for this country today is that people should come to realize, first that science is not latter-day witchcraft but simply a process of disciplined thought and experiment; and second that technology is neither a mystery nor beneath contempt, but simply the translation of knowledge into practical advantages in everyday life.

It was true, particularly in technological education, that in the second half of the nineteenth century we were still living in the first stage of the industrial revolution, although this revolution had by this time gone well into its second stage. If we are to behave responsibly in a modern democracy; if we are going to approach the problem of power and its concentration in any satisfactory spirit; it will not be because some cheap newspaper has worked up an inflammation about some issue or other. It will be because the ordinary boy and girl knows a little bit about some of these things and can begin to make reasoned and sensible judgements.

The Christian will agree with this. And he will add that when we talk about 'education in an age of technology' we do not mean simply education in the technical aspects of a particular job, nor a formal knowledge of the changes which have taken place in the last hundred years; but we do also imply an education for responsibility. Now the only kind of responsibility that is of any use is a religious one, however bravely we clothe it in high-sounding phrases. This is why Christians ought to interest themselves in such matters. Historically education was for centuries almost exclusively a concern of the Church, so that our older colleges are described as 'places of sound learning and religious education'. There is plenty of indication that in our more modern technological institutes this emphasis has been largely obliterated. We must teach the budding technologist and technician to think not only of the technical details of their jobs, but also of the obligation which they should accept with them.

We have been concerned with four aspects of contemporary life where science and technology have already made profound changes. These were the future use of power, particularly in relation to the underdeveloped countries; the provision of food, and its relation to the rise of population; the changes in family life in Britain which are bound up with a higher standard of living; and the inferences which this allows us to make for education. In every case we could pick out the ways in which the first industrial revolution showed itself. Some of these were good; others, because of human fallibility or inertness, were bad. We could also catch some glimpse of the way in which these changes were being transcended in the second industrial revolution. In order to ensure that we made the best use of our new knowledge, a Christian judgement and, sometimes, a Christian initiative were needed. And of course the penalty for wrong-doing is now much more severe than it ever was before.

CHAPTER FIVE

Science and Technology as Unifying Influences

IT IS WIDELY agreed that our Western community is in a disintegrating state, and that its restoration to wholeness requires at the very least the acceptance on a wide scale of some dominant cohesive belief. Such an ideology, if sufficiently central, might serve not only to stay the process of disintegration, but equally to be the foundation of some new order of society. If we reject— as surely most of us in the West must reject—the totalitarian solution, whether that be interpreted as Communism, Fascism, or extreme Capitalism, it behoves us to search out some alternative mode of thought, deep enough to command the thinking consent of the few as well as the unthinking and largely emotional consent of the many.

There is an increasing number of people who believe that in the Christian faith there is to be found a sufficient dynamic of this kind. But it is equally certain that there is no reasonable hope of its present acceptance on a sufficiently large scale. Previous chapters in this book have shown some of the mental adjustments that are necessary before we are ready to cope with the intellectual and social problems of a mechanized atomic-age civilization; and in our closing chapter we shall have more to say about the Christian's contribution. Other movements of thought are more evidently insufficient.

Thus literature, 'culture' and the arts are too restricted in their appeal to capture the loyalty of the non-intellectual; nationalism, or any other return to the ways of the past (such as Gandhi's cult of the loom in India) does violence to the mind of the intellectual. It is not surprising, therefore, that in many people there has grown up the feeling that science, or perhaps technology, is to be the buttress against disintegration, and the centre-pin of man's restoration. Bearing in mind the contents of our earlier chapters, let us consider this claim, beginning first with science, and then passing on to technology.

Now there can be no doubt concerning the international character of science. 'We assert the international character of science: it is a world-wide republic of the mind', was the claim made by a group of about twenty Fellows of the Royal Society, and others, in 1951; and their document continued: 'Scientists form one fraternity, united in a common attempt to understand nature and a common concern for human betterment.' This is all most valid and correct. In this sense scientists know none of the conventional intellectual boundaries: Thus Eddington, in the Preface to his lectures *The Expanding Universe*, writes:

This is an international conference, and I have chosen an international subject. I shall speak of the theoretical work of Einstein of Germany, de Sitter of Holland, Lemaitre of Belgium. For observational data I turn to the Americans, Slipher, Hubble, Humason, recalling however that the vitally important datum of distance is found by a method which we owe to Hertzsprung of Denmark. As I must not trouble you with mathematical analysis I have to pass over Levi-Civita of Italy, whose methods and ideas we employ. But

I must refer especially to the new interest which arises in the subject through its linkage with wave-mechanics: as a representative name in wave-mechanics, I mention that of its originator, de Broglie of France.

Those words were written in 1932, before World War II. But they are still true. The tremendous conferences on the Peaceful Uses of Atomic Energy, and the world-wide ramifications of the International Geophysical Year are further reminders of that same spirit. Even in wartime scientists have often been able to show this wider loyalty. Reference has already been made in an earlier chapter to Sir Humphrey Davy's visit to France during our war with that country in the nineteenth century. But a century earlier, in 1779, when Britain was at war with America, their scientist Benjamin Franklin sent out a message to all American warships telling them of Captain Cook's ship exploring in the South Seas, calling it 'an Undertaking truly laudable in itself, as the Increase of Geographical Knowledge facilitates the Communications between distant Nations . . .' and recommending that if this ship should fall into their hands, they should not 'consider her as an Enemy, nor suffer any Plunder to be made of the Effects contain'd in her'.

The international fraternity of scientists is a very genuine one, as all of us know who have any occasion to take part in visits or conferences abroad. In part this is because we are concerned in 'playing the same game', and have much the same equipment for it. But I believe that it goes deeper than this. The binding force in science springs from the true nature of science and its origin. Thus Professor Polanyi, in the opening words of his Riddell Lectures in 1946, *Science, Faith and Society*:

I shall re-examine here the suppositions underlying our belief in science, and propose to show that they are more extensive than is usually thought. They will appear to co-extend with the entire spiritual foundations of man and to go to the very root of his social existence. Hence, I will urge, our belief in science should be regarded as a token of much wider convictions.

All this is quite true. But it is not enough on which to base the unity of a civilization. Very few of us would wish to resuscitate Plato's dream of world government by the philosopher kings—now presumably the world's leading scientists. It is remarkable that in Britain the establishment of a Minister for Science should have been greeted by such careful, and non-emotional, inquiries as to his real function. Scientists are, on the average, no better than other people at the business of politics; and they are frequently worse. Political aims are unlikely to coincide with scientific aims, since they start from essentially distinct assumptions. Men of science are, as a rule, first of all men of science. As one of the participants in the Pugwash Conferences put it: 'They may want a scientific community, but they do not want a scientific party.' There is immense value in the international meeting of scientists, representative as they are of the modes of thought and the cultural heritage of their own peoples. But real scientific knowledge is too sparse, the whole scientific movement is too broken up and specialized for more than a handful of scientists to possess a wide enough grasp of its many sections. I can see that science can help us by pointing to its own internal cohesion, and its happy international practice. But it is too refined to do more than this. The three biggest errors in scientific humanism are the assumptions that everybody can do what scientists can do (though presumably without their knowledge); that scientists are themselves capable of right action without any outside help; and that science is the only true way of knowing. The first of these is educationally false, and ultimately rejects true democracy. The second would lead us to the patently absurd conclusion that our laboratories should be full of saints: the third denies so much of art and beauty, love and fear that it is totally unacceptable to those who know something of the nature of man as a child of God.

Science—alone—cannot be the cohesive force in our modern world. But what about technology? This is not so specialized and remote. Thus, for every person who understands Einstein's famous relation $E = mc^2$ connecting the mass and energy of a moving particle, there are millions who experience the products of technology, either in the form of new gadgets or new medicines. A former Beckly lecturer put it in these words:

The salesman has penetrated to the remotest corners, and the products of Lancashire, Birmingham and Coventry, and also the United States, are ubiquitous. On a recent visit to Central Africa I heard of a missionary who declared that he had often been in districts where the Gospel had never been preached, but never anywhere where you could not buy a sewing-machine on the hire-purchase system.

Technology is seen in its workings in places where the science from which it now stems is quite unknown. It is indeed universal. A recent writer has attempted to summarize the main headings under which all technological operations can be grouped. They are three in number:

(a) those aimed at raising the material standard of living,

(b) those aimed at increasing leisure, or eliminating dull and unnecessary work,

(c) those aimed at replacing bad technology by better technology.

These headings are truly universal, and would have applied to our great-grandfathers as well as to ourselves, to Communists or Christians. There is nothing in them which, by itself, should divide mankind into conflicting groups. It is not surprising that in recent years there has been an attempt to claim that technological humanism can do what scientific humanism cannot do. In the world of the second industrial revolution the only humanism which is appropriate is one that 'confers values on the automatic factory, the aeroplane, television and the popular Press; it must have something to offer the sort of man who a century ago could neither read nor write, and who now reads only the popular Press and listens to the Light Programme of the BBC'. It is suggested that technology may hold the key to general culture because, 'unlike science, it involves an understanding of popular art and commerce and psychology, something of morals and justice, and some skill in the art of communication'.

There is a good deal of truth in these claims. And as a recent editorial in *Nature* has reminded us, technology is a much more human enterprise than science. It concerns itself with the creative acts of modern man; so that to enthuse about Gothic churches and Tudor halls without even a glance at a Viscount aeroplane or a stressed concrete bridge is inexcusable if we claim that only the former are creative arts of man. So also technology has its own standards of excellence, and when we complain of the shoddiness of many mass-produced articles, we are describing a weakness in the public rather than in technology: where high standards are insisted upon, as in aeroplanes, cameras, or gold watches, there is great excellence. Finally, technology involves the handling of ideas and the acceptance of some sort of values. If I want to make a new detergent, I shall require some practical and some formal knowledge of chemistry; but when I have made it, I shall have to judge how best to offer it to the public, what claims I may reasonably make for it as compared with those of my rivals; I must know how the public responds to different types of salesmanship, and I must judge the extent to which an outlay of money in improving the product, or in making it better known, is justified by such returns as I may hope to gain. This requires attention to morals and other ethical considerations.

These are the claims now being made by the believers in technological humanism. We do ill to reject them. Sometimes it seems to me that technology and science are now the only fields of human endeavour where almost complete agreement between East and West is not entirely unthinkable. Who would suggest that East and West could agree on matters touching the sculpture of Henry Moore or the novels of Boris Pasternak? But they can agree about the design of an artificial satellite, and independently reach similar conclusions about the best way to propel it into space. A very remarkable though not in any way sensational illustration of this occurred in the first United Nations Conference on the Peaceful Uses of Atomic Energy in 1955. At this conference a large amount of hitherto secret research was made public. It appeared that no less than five countries had independently been developing techniques for the extraction of uranium from ores that contained only a small percentage of the metal. This is a difficult process, but almost identical techniques had been developed.

The suggestion that technology may provide the cohesive force in modern society may be set within an historical perspective. Sir Eric Ashby has pointed out that twice in history European civilization has been one fabric, and twice it has been torn. Science and technology contributed to its destruction, but 'in science and invention lies our hope for its future'. The first destruction was by the barbarians who destroyed the Roman civilization, notable for its cosmopolitan ideas, from which the local and provincial spirit was strikingly absent. Later, in the Renaissance the traffic of ideas again revived, but the directing influence was no longer theology or the Church, but Natural Philosophy and the study of nature. First in the exchange of ideas among scientists, then in the publications of their newly established societies, science and the universities played a notable part in establishing a unity. The second industrial revolution and our two World Wars have shattered this; there is an almost complete break between the university professor and the rank and file of Europeans. Our future hope—so says Sir Eric Ashby—lies in cohesion among whole populations of Europeans, not solely among a handful of university teachers. Let us make what use we can of the unity among these latter; but let us not suppose that it is enough. Technology belongs to the masses: let us build on this.

What is the Christian commentary on this claim for

technological humanism? In a single sentence it is this, that technology does indeed provide some basis for joint action, but that because the diagnosis of our society which the humanists propose is not deep enough, technology alone is not sufficient.

Two examples will show what this means. Let us return for a moment to the man who had just devised a new detergent, and wanted to sell it to the public. If we grant that the problems of advertising contain a moral and ethical aspect, can we expect him to solve them within technology alone? Obviously we cannot, even if we are prepared to include in the term technology the social sciences such as market surveys and consumer research. These will provide him with the data for a decision, but they will not decide. One of the advertisers who spends a lot of money buying time on commercial television told me recently that not only he himself, but many of his friends, and rivals, were becoming concerned because they did not know how to control, or judge, the advertisement processes. How subtly should they appeal to sex, and how much should their advertisements accept, or pretend to accept, a lower standard of morality or a Hollywood relationship between husband and wife? There is no answer in technology: and ultimately therefore there is no cohesion.

My second example concerns the problem of the under-developed countries. There are great needs, some of which were described in the last chapter. The developed countries of the West can supply some of these needs, and by taxation or otherwise, they can offer to provide money and capital to initiate the 'industrial take-off' that is necessary before the poorer countries can start effective development. But this alone is not sufficient.

If the gap in living standards is to be closed, then human sympathy as well as economic insight will be required. Science and technology can achieve great results; they can spread goodwill and tolerance. But behind them, however often it may remain unrecognized, is an older and deeper faith—of men in mankind.

We can carry this argument a stage farther. Whether the undeveloped countries do or do not achieve the industrialization which they need will not depend entirely on whether Britain and America offer them the one thousand million pounds annually which we showed in the last chapter was a necessary element in this process. The relationship between countries, as the relationship between rich and poor, is not purely economic and financial. It is spiritual. So the malaise and the divisions which cut across our unity will not be cured solely by economic and financial aid—any more than poverty is cured by charitable subscription. Sir Charles Snow in his recent Rede Lecture at Cambridge, *The Two Cultures*, has described how easily technology is learnt, and has shown how in the second industrial revolution there will be a 'technological revolution' everywhere within fifty years. We begin to see it already in India and China. But for its proper development, this will need more than capital or money; it will need people. To help in the industrialization of India alone, we need to provide between ten and twenty thousand engineers. These must be men who 'would shrug off every trace of paternalism . . . men who will muck in as colleagues, who will pass on what they know, do an honest technical job, and get out'. But it is not only engineers who are wanted. There will be all the supporting groups, of doctors, nurses, secretaries, teachers. All these also must be people who will 'pass on what they know, do an honest technical job, and get out'.

Where will such people be found? Technology alone will not produce them, and those who go abroad to get rich more easily than is possible at home are scarcely likely to fulfil these conditions. Here we see that technology needs something added: it needs the personal drive that comes from the conviction that this is God's world —and so it goes back to a proper view of man. G. K. Chesterton's advice to the man seeking to find lodgings— 'Do not ask about the food, but ask the landlady what is her philosophy of life'—is apposite here. In the last resort, the question whether the technological revolution will come happily or not to the undeveloped countries will not depend just on an adequate supply of funds, nor of technologists, technicians, science teachers and the like, though of course these are necessary. It will depend upon whether the personal relationships involved are recognized and dealt with—the sacrifice among the wealthy nations, the acceptance of charity among the poorer ones, the mutual trust which alone makes co-operation fruitful. All these are possible only if we have a worthy view of man. Technology, without this, may do infinite harm. But with it, it may become a tool in the shaping of the Kingdom of Heaven on earth.

I would like to draw out of this discussion one con-clusion of the greatest importance. I believe that there is no greater missionary need today than that young men and women should see this work, particularly but not wholly in India and Africa, as a Christian vocation. Technology will come to the backward parts of the world: it will influence them as profoundly as we know that it has influenced us. There could scarcely be a finer vocation than to see that when it comes, it comes supported and interpreted by the best spiritual insights that we have. This is true missionary activity, whether or not it boasts that official title. Sometimes I have the conviction that this kind of missionary work is as important, perhaps more important, than the more conventional work of the missionary societies. It may even be that the coming of the second industrial revolution to India in the next fifty years represents our last great opportunity, humanly speaking, for the evangelization of that huge country. The technologist can go where the old-time missionary cannot; he can say and do things which the other cannot; and people will listen to him. I should like to feel that here in Britain we were training thousands of people for this task. For it is desperately important that the industrialization of India shall be established in the right spirit. The American physicist Arthur Compton tells of a meeting with the Indian scientist Sir Shanti Bhatnagar. They were talking of the future for India, and Sir Shanti turned to Professor Compton, saying: 'There is one thing that you in the West can teach us in the East. It is something that matters tremendously. Show us that it is good to live in an industrialized community.' In the deepest level of understanding, only those who have seen the Incarnation, and know in their lives the great Christian doctrine of Creation, are big enough for this job. The Christian need not be afraid of technology: rather must he welcome it. But he must add to it that which it lacks, and without which it can never become a unifying influence in the world.

Epilogue

MANY OF THE things discussed in the earlier part of this book will seem perfectly obvious to most of us. But they do not appear so to a surprisingly large number of people. The claim that science and technology are a concern of the spirit would be attacked from both sides—by Christians and by technologists. For example, Christian people do not see that the Church must be involved. A few months ago I had occasion to write a religious article for a national newspaper. In it I spoke about the atoms of which a human body is composed. Shortly afterwards I received a letter from someone, upbraiding me for talking about atoms in such an article. 'I adore the Church,' he said, 'but why did you have to introduce atoms in your article? I had to go to a dictionary to see what they meant.' And again, on the other side, the claim of the Christian community to make its voice heard in industrial and economic discussion is opposed by non-Christians, on the grounds that religion is one department of life, like art or science, and it becomes an offensive busybody as soon as it interferes in any other sphere. Archbishop Temple tells the story of what happened in the disastrous Coal Strike of 1926, when a group of Bishops attempted to bring the Government, coal-owners and miners together so that a free discussion could take place, and some solution might emerge. Mr Baldwin, then Prime Minister, objected, asking how the Bishops would like it if he referred to the Iron and Steel Federation the revision of the Athanasian Creed. This was acclaimed as a legitimate score!

What, then, can the Christian do? I would like to suggest three ways in which he can help to fulfil his responsibility.

First, we really must see what is happening. The second industrial revolution—the union of science and invention—is one of the most astounding phases of human development. Our new technology, with the continuing growth that followed the 'take-off' outlined in the last chapter, is quite unique. The economist Eugene Staley has pointed out where this uniqueness chiefly lies: it is not in our gadgets but in our technique for using one lot of gadgets to produce another lot, rather in the manner of a rolling snowball. The most significant invention of modern times, he says, is not electronic communication, or nuclear energy, or antibiotics, but 'organized scientific research and development . . . we have a technology for producing new technology'. This ability which we have now learnt, that we can build machines that will themselves build machines, constitutes the heart of today's technological revolution. If we believe in the doctrines of Creation and Incarnation, we cannot deny that the Atomic Age is part of God's world. We cannot act responsibly in it unless we know what it is. Therefore we must see, and become aware of what is happening. A policy of isolation is here equivalent to abandonment of any hope of leading. Such an abandonment may cost the Church one more large slice not only of her membership, but of her invisible influence. There is good reason to believe that it was an isolationist philosophy of this kind during the Evangelical Revival which lost the Church its leadership of the working masses. In the words of Canon Raven: 'Thanks to it, social reform followed Marx and not Maurice, and the masses lost all confidence in evangelical religion.'

Secondly we must see this revolution as a spiritual one as well as a material one. Here we have more help than we sometimes imagine from the scientists. The theoretical physicist Hans Bethe described the views of the Los Alamos scientists on the moral and humane problems of their wartime work for the atomic bomb as follows:

I am unhappy to admit that during the war—at least—I did not pay much attention to this. We had a job to do and a very hard one. The first thing we wanted to do was to get the job done. It seemed to us most important to contribute to victory in the way we could. Only when our labours were finally completed when the bomb dropped on Japan, only then or a little before then maybe, did we start thinking about the moral implications.

Professor J. R. Oppenheimer summed this up in an unforgettable sentence: 'In some crude sense, which no vulgarity, no humour, no overstatement can quite extinguish, the physicists have known sin, and this is a knowledge which they cannot lose.'

It should be easier for us to see this interplay of the scientific and the spiritual. Sometimes as I brood over the problems that lie in front of the next fifty years— the feeding of a hungry world in which nearly one half is always on the edge of starvation; the raising of the standard of life among the underprivileged, so that they are no longer ravaged by illiteracy, squalor, and disease; the control and peaceful uses of atomic power; the restraining of the world's rapidly increasing population— I realize that under the conditions of today these are not just technological and scientific problems. The

American Chairman of the National Conference of
Christians and Jews who wrote, 'If 600 scientists working
together could produce the atomic bomb, then 600
scientists should be put to work on the job of inter-
group hatreds', was a long way from understanding how
racial discrimination can be countered. Nor are these
great problems just political or diplomatic (though they
are most certainly both of these). They are essentially
moral and religious problems. We shall not solve them
by scientific know-how alone, or diplomatic expertise
alone, or even religious conviction alone. We shall solve
them as we bring all three together to bear on the
decisions that have to be made. For the faith in one
another without which international relations turn into
anarchy, the risks which have to be taken in allowing
scientists to conduct their research without knowing to
what strange new secrets they will be led, the insight
into the true nature of man without which you cannot
plan for his welfare, the sensitiveness to his personality
without which even your proffered help may be rejected
—these are some of the great spiritual contributions that
religion brings. It is one of the gravest temptations of
our age, to pigeon-hole and classify its problems. The
Christian has the responsibility to say that it is folly so
to do.

I said that there were three contributions which the
Christian has to make in our present situation. The first
was to recognize what was happening in the new industrial revolution: the second was to show that the
problems thus raised were not merely technological, but
were compounded of science, technology, politics, and
faith. I now come to the third. It is for the Christian
to set the pattern of thought against which decisions

and action may be judged. The Christian really is the leaven in the lump. Only those who know the inner nature of Man, and the peculiar ways in which God transforms a man's mind by the renewing power of His Spirit, and the status which God confers upon him that he may be called a child of God, are big enough to speak to the condition of today. Scientists cannot think out their problems alone; when they try to decide what to do with their own inventions, as in the case of Fuchs, on their own responsibility and without appeal to something beyond, it is not long before disaster follows. Nor can politicians achieve the ends that they desire, despite their claim that 'politics is the art of getting things done', without the appropriate climate of opinion. This climate is something they are almost powerless to create. Yet it is one of the greatest contributions that Christian people can make, if they bestir themselves.

We could carry this argument a stage farther. Any community can only function as a unity when it is dominated by some central idea, or common objective. It is, of course, the recognition of this which had led to the various Communist Five-Year Plans. In the words of an Industrial Chaplain: 'the crux of democracy is the faith that the common objective in our industrial society must be agreed by all its members rather than imposed upon them. We have to stand or fall by that faith. That is our present crisis (in relation particularly to Communism) and that is where the Christian Church must come in.' The role of the Christian community as such is not to do the science, or devise the technology, or form some new political party: it is to see the need of all these, to welcome them as gifts of God; and then to think creatively, bringing all these aspects of human toil together using for this purpose all the clues and the signposts that I have been describing. Science and technology are needed, and in the using of them on a sufficiently imaginative scale we may come to see more clearly the way that God works through them. But alone, like patriotism, they are not enough. Bring them into live contact with our sensitive Christian insights, and there is fashioned one of the best tools in all the bag for the building of the Kingdom of Heaven here on earth. Here indeed is the one great dominant purpose, big enough and worthy enough and sufficiently demanding to become the cohesive force which modern society needs.

There is still one thing to add. It refers to one of the Christian virtues which has a singularly important significance for times like our own, of unparalleled opportunity tempered by uncertainty and fear. I am thinking of hope—Christian hope. In its ultimate analysis this springs from a belief in the three great doctrines of the Church—creation, incarnation, and redemption. It is out of the meeting of these three that we come to believe in the future, and to know that it is God's future in which we are believing. It is only because of hope that we shall dare to attempt those great changes in industry and family life and international commerce, without which no permanent and equitable peace can ever grow. It is only because of hope that we can drive out that worst of all companions, fear; or work without the expectation that we shall live to see the fruits of our efforts. It is by hope that we continue to be flexible, and open-minded, free from the chains of temporal history, free to accept new knowledge and new power as they come to us. Hope is one of the greatest gifts which the Christian has to give to the secular world. As the

Director of the Bristol Institute of Education said a
year or two ago:

The contemporary scene is dark and the outlook for the future
is far from clear. It would seem as if only great statesman-
ship or great good fortune could prevent the outbreak of a
kind of global civil war. Yet I am reminded nevertheless of
some words that were inscribed in the porch of an English
village church at a time when our own country was ravaged
by its worst civil war. They are these: 'In the year 1642, when
most things sacred were either demolished or profaned, this
church was built by one whose singular praise it is to have
done the best things in the worst times and to have hoped
them in the most calamitous.'